IN SEARCH OF
JOSEPHINE BAKER

John Kirby Abraham

First Published 2001
Second Edition 2003

ISBN 1-904018-72-6

Published by

Pen Press Publishers Ltd
39 – 41 North Rd
Islington
London N7 9DP

IN SEARCH OF
JOSEPHINE BAKER

The only sincere tribute paid to the great lady whom I used to call, and still do call 'Maman'. Thank you, John, for bringing her back into the limelight in such a sincere way.

Love, Akio
(the eldest of the Rainbow Tribe)

Monsieur Akio Bouillon

Acknowledgements

I wish to thank the following people who gave their time to talk about their relationship with Josephine Baker:

Madame Caroline Dudley-Delteil, Monsieur Marcel Sauvage, Madame Mathilde Légitimus, Monsieur Paul Colin, Madame Margarette Wallace, Monsieur Georges Tabet, Monsieur Jean Wiéner, Monsieur Pierre Spiers, Monsieur Bernard Dimey, Monsieur Jean Clément, Monsieur Joseph Bouillon,

and also for their able assistance, Krystyna, Lilian, Juliet and Charlie.

Contents

Preface

The stage door of most traditional theatres is often hidden out of sight of the front of house public entrance. The *Entrée des Artistes* of the huge Champs-Élysées Theatre in Paris, and the stage door of the smaller Bobino Theatre in the Montparnasse quarter, were typically obscure entrances for goods and personnel. Performers would enter backstage to become transformed into entertainers. When their presentation was over they would leave their stage persona behind and return to everyday life, unless they belonged to that species of artiste who are always acting, on both sides of the stage door. This is the story of one such artiste whose whole life was one long strenuous performance, on and off the stage.

The two Parisian theatres mentioned above saw, respectively, the beginning and the end of Josephine Baker's long international career. From remote origins in the United States she achieved overnight celebrity in Paris and toured the world. France was the stage on which she played out her exuberant life and she always returned to her adopted European home.

Josephine Baker brought her natural talents out of the theatre and into her everyday life. She was always on view, unconsciously or not, performing for those around her. Such a never-ending performance gave both great pleasure, and not a little anxiety, to all who came into contact with her.

When I first heard her recording of *J'ai Deux Amours* in London, I was spellbound and astonished. Many years later I came face to face with the voice on the record when I pushed open an unmarked door at the back of the Bobino Theatre in Paris. She was sitting on an upright wooden chair singing alone to a tape recorder. When the door slammed shut behind me she turned and said brightly, 'Hello!' I took her hand and said, '*Bonjour, Madame Baker!*' It was the end of a quest. The year was 1975... the year she died.

Prologue

Ailleurs, disait-on, il y a des femmes; à Paris il y a la Femme.[*]

King Edward VII once told Mistinguett, who reigned over the French music hall for more than half a century, 'It's through its women that one gets to know Paris. It's the air of Paris that creates the Parisienne – who is hardly ever a Parisienne by birth.'

Josephine Baker, who once naively remarked that she 'preferred kings to all other men', arrived in Europe fifteen years too late to charm the British monarch. Far from being Parisian by birth, she was not even French and couldn't speak a word of the language when she arrived in Paris in 1925. Yet this African American from Missouri, whom Parisians acclaimed, came to personify the 'Parisienne' for audiences on four continents, and earned from Colette the epithet, *'la plus parisienne des panthères'*.

Before leaving America at the age of nineteen, Josephine had moved mainly among black Americans. The first white Frenchmen she encountered were waiters at the Old Plantation Club in New York where she worked as a dancer. To her surprise they treated black artistes as equals, called her a *rigolote* – a comic -- and proceeded to show her a photograph of the Eiffel Tower. Preferring it to the Statue of Liberty, whose reputed favours she had learned to mistrust, and because it simply looked to her like a big toy, she resolved to pay it a visit one day. She had been told – and believed – that in France all were free, if not also equal and fraternal.

The chance to put this to the test came sooner than she expected. Within months Josephine was offered a contract to dance in Paris and, together with two dozen other black artistes, she sailed for Europe.

If Josephine Baker's life had been invented, it would seem on

---

[*] 'Elsewhere, it is said, there are women; in Paris, there is Woman.'

the surface like a rags-to-riches fairy tale, or the scenario of a musical film of the Thirties. The traditional ingredients are all present: a stage-struck teenager who leaves home to join a dance troupe; discovery in the chorus line of a music hall; overnight success in Paris followed by stardom at the Folies Bergère, world tours, international acclaim, and a final triumphant 'comeback' at the end of a lifelong career.

There is even a Prince Charming (in reality an orchestra leader whom she marries) to bring them prosperity and happiness at their castle in south-west France. There Josephine acts as Fairy Godmother to a family of adopted children, when she is not flying off to Buenos Aires or Berlin to entertain the ranks of international café society.

To this script should be added the saga of her service as an intelligence agent in the French Resistance during World War II, which gained her national honours and decorations from the French President and the lasting gratitude of the Allies.

The story of Josephine Baker's life is generously endowed with crowned heads and nobility, foreign travel, espionage, champagne and jazz. It spans the Roaring Twenties, through the age of anxiety and war, to our present epoch of mass diversity in entertainment and the arts.

But this story of a black Cinderella who leaped social and professional hurdles to achieve fame and fortune also has its sombre side in which she paid a heavy tribute for her racial origins.

Josephine Baker's life is also the story of a black St. Louis washerwoman's daughter, of mixed European and African ancestry, who turned her back on her birthright and chose a career in which her dark skin became an asset. With the money she earned as an international entertainer, she founded a multiracial community in France for children of different ethnic backgrounds.

Unlike the average fairy tale however, illness, humiliation and near disaster pursued her. Real-life demons kept knocking at her door and creditors' bailiffs eventually succeeded in evicting the 'Rainbow Tribe' of adopted children from their castle and closing down the village.

But even here a fairy-tale element persisted. At the last moment the evicted family was saved from disaster by a real-life prince and princess who intervened to offer a home in their principality on the warm, inviting shores of the Mediterranean. From the black ghetto of Boxcar Town in St. Louis, where she was born in poverty, Josephine found final sanctuary in Monaco.

The irony of her situation, living penniless among millionaires in Monte Carlo, was not lost on her creditors. Approaching the age of seventy, Josephine was obliged to undertake a series of gruelling singing tours to pay off her debts. The sparkle and verve of her last stage appearances concealed her chagrin at having failed to create the permanent inter-racial community for which she had devoted so much effort.

But Josephine's determination never faltered. She was still making plans to recreate somewhere – anywhere – her vanished community, when she died of a heart attack in Paris in 1975, an ageing but ageless artiste in full possession of her powers, a voluntary exile in her adopted country, celebrating the fiftieth anniversary of her arrival in Europe. Of her passing, one writer exclaimed, 'It was like a magnificent sunset!'

As the last of the great French *meneuses* of Grand Revue, Josephine Baker's life was a show business success story, a cautionary tale for all who imagine that they can change the world single-handed, and a salutary reminder of the continuing struggle against racial discrimination.

Chapter One
The Twenties and *La Revue Nègre*

The Twenties

> De 1920 à 1930 nous étions tous convaincus que nous allions
> créer quelque chose, nous n'avions pas la prétention de changer le
> monde, mais de lui donner un aspect et un esprit nouveau.[*]

Florent Fels

The decade known as the Twenties has been described as 'one long party to which everyone was invited'. Many countries and capital cities shared in the general surge of well-being that followed the end of the First World War. Across the Atlantic the period was called the Roaring Twenties; in Germany they celebrated *Die Goldenen Zwanziger Jahre*, while in London it became the Gay Twenties. The city that led the fashion in the arts and entertainment, and became the focus for post-war pleasure seekers, was Paris, where 'Les Années Folles', or the Crazy Years, lasted until 1929.

Paris in the Twenties attracted people from all over the world. Writers, artists, entertainers and intellectuals of every nationality converged on the French capital to make the city the most cosmopolitan in Europe. One newcomer arrived when the party was at its height. She took the city by storm and stayed to make France her home. She was a young coloured dancer from St. Louis, USA, and her name was Josephine Baker.

Arriving in Paris in the Twenties, one was immediately

---

[*] 'From 1920 to 1930, we were all convinced that we were going to create
something. We didn't set out to change the world, but to give it a new look and
spirit.'

infected with the atmosphere of intense gaiety and excitement. With the return of peace a mood of euphoria had swept across Europe, and the resulting resurgence of energy and enthusiasm had produced experiments in living at all levels of society. The air was charged with new ideas and innovation was the keynote of the day.

Paris in the Twenties, with its huge immigrant population, had become the intellectual and artistic capital of the post-war world. Painters, poets and musicians found themselves at the forefront of an unparalleled wave of freedom of expression, and they became the self-appointed prophets of the age. The café tables of Montparnasse and Montmartre were crowded each day with multilingual groups discussing new theories of art, literature – and life! The greater their originality, the greater their momentary success with the crowd.

Surrealism had supplanted Dadaism as the dominant artistic movement. The poets André Breton, Paul Eluard and Louis Aragon proclaimed, 'Cleanliness is the luxury of the poor.' Then to confound and delight the public they added, 'True Dadas are against Dada!' The prolific novelist, Maurice Dekobra, who had just published *La Madone des Sleepings*, wrote, 'Paris is synonymous with freedom. Foreigners are delighted not to find a detective in the corridor of their hotel who asks them, "Is the woman in your room your legal wife?"' The English novelist, Aldous Huxley, who frequently crossed the Channel to France, extolled in his writing 'the tireless rhythm of jazz... the sweet and piercing saxophone like a revelation from heaven...' And André Fraigneau reminded his readers that 'it was the Negro epoch, the jazz epoch, with swept-up hair, tame cubism, sexual daring, gratuitous behaviour and senseless suicides'.

From a Left Bank café terrace one might see the daring English socialite, Nancy Cunard, on the arm of a Negro companion, or the brilliant Jean Cocteau with his retinue of admirers. An American journalist named Hemingway would be talking about his second novel, to be called *The Sun Also Rises*, while not far away James Joyce and Gertrude Stein were independently performing verbal acrobatics in their own writing.

While portly Gertrude Stein called the younger generation

after the war a 'lost generation', another American, the agile Isadora Duncan, was leaping about on the stage in bare feet and flowing robes, declaring, 'I am not a dancer and have never been a dancer, but I have been the initiator of a new mode of living!' And while unemployed hunger marchers were converging on London and Paris, Professor Coué of France was prescribing the daily repetition of the litany, 'Every day, in every way, I am getting better and better!' Truly, the epoch of the Twenties marked the renaissance of the twentieth century.

La Revue Nègre arrives

When nineteen-year-old Josephine Baker arrived in Europe as a member of a coloured American dance company, she knew nothing of the vast social changes that had been set in motion since the end of the war, or of the kind of life she would encounter in Paris. When she was offered the chance in New York to join a coloured troupe to go to Paris, she accepted, despite the uncertainties involved. She had little to lose. She had heard many agreeable things about France, not least that black people were treated as equals among the white population. That alone was a sufficient incentive for her to escape the racial discrimination in America of which she was already aware.

Josephine's arrival in the French capital, as one of a group of American Negro performers, thrust her into an entirely different world from that of the non-white American vaudeville theatre. Not only was there an insatiable demand for every kind of novelty and amusement, but the city also offered unlimited scope for those with talent and initiative, regardless of race, creed or colour.

Paris in 1925 was not as we know it today, with its maelstrom of traffic streaming between tall office buildings and historic monuments blackened by pollution. At its outer limits Paris was still a city of 'villages' or *quartiers*, each with its own special character. Social life was orderly. People strolled for pleasure, or sat and talked at café tables set out on terraces or in tiny squares under trees. Social intercourse took place at a personal level in surroundings of a human scale.

Nearer to the centre of the capital there was greater activity. The last remaining section of the *Grands Boulevards*, planned by

Baron Haussmann for Napoléon III fifty years earlier, had just been opened. Carriages and spluttering automobiles paraded in a slow procession between the Étoile and the Place de la République. Within the broad arc of the new boulevards, provincial and foreign visitors were offered an unimaginable variety of diversion and amusement. The lights of shops, arcades, restaurants, theatres and music halls beckoned and dazzled the crowds who flocked to the city centre.

Few, if any, of the half-million American tourists visiting Europe in 1925 were aware of the arrival in Paris that autumn of a theatre troupe of twenty-five of their coloured compatriots. If they had known, it is unlikely they would have gone out of their way to see a group of unknown artistes from Harlem performing on the stage of a Paris music hall. The city had other, more typically French attractions to offer foreign visitors.

Many had come to Paris that year to visit the *Exposition Internationale des Arts Décoratifs et Industriels Modernes*, popularly known as the Art Deco Exhibition, which had opened in April, and whose pavilions were strung out along the banks of the River Seine. Here, among the modernistic and functional exhibits of applied art, visitors could admire the fountains and gaily lit river boats of the celebrated couturier, Paul Poiret, dedicated to *Amours*, *Délices* and *Orgues*, and decorated by the painter, Raoul Dufy. If one stepped on board the vessel named *Amours*, one could actually see Maître Poiret, seated at his perfume piano which emitted different scents when he played certain chords. For less refined tastes, visitors could pitch a seated Negro into a tank of water when a plank was pulled from under him and a lever manipulated after dropping a coin into a slot.

The arrival of the American *Revue Nègre* troupe, of which Josephine Baker was a member, was part of that flow of American talent which had first started to cross the Atlantic at the beginning of the century, and which the war had interrupted. Ever since John Philip Sousa had brought ragtime to Europe at the turn of the century, white, coloured and black American performers had appeared in European capitals. Negro American dancers had demonstrated the Cakewalk in Paris in 1904, and coloured dancers had appeared at the Moulin Rouge before the First World

War. Irving Berlin's rousing 'Alexander's Ragtime Band' had helped popularise syncopation and ragtime during the war.

It was not until the French music hall artiste, Gaby Deslys, brought a complete Negro jazz band back with her from New York in 1917, to accompany her in her frenetic dances with Harry Pilcer at the Casino de Paris, that the word 'jazz' passed into common usage in Europe, and that particular brand of music became a permanent ingredient of popular dance music.

Jazz rhythms began to make their impact on composers of so-called serious music. Georges Auric was never to forget his first exposure to jazz during visits to the Casino de Paris in 1917, and Francis Poulenc wrote his *Rhapsodie Nègre*, with its tribal dance, the same year. A little later, Darius Milhaud composed *Caramel Mou*, described as a 'shimmy' for a jazz band, to which Jean Cocteau contributed suitable words. While Milhaud exploited jazz rhythms in his piano suite, *Saudades do Brasil*, Claude Debussy's 'Gollywogs' Cakewalk' testified to Sousa's passage through Europe, and Stravinsky's 'Ragtime for Eleven Instruments' recalled that composer's travels between Moscow, Paris and the United States.

If the 'Original' Dixieland Jazz Band, made up of white musicians(!), had offered London audiences a taste of black American popular music in 1919, the real thing was to be found in Paris in the Twenties. Among the four million American soldiers who had embarked for Europe during the war, many black musicians among them had stayed on in Paris and other European capitals, to play in bars and cabarets where the colour of their skin was considered an asset in the exercise of their talents.

In 1921, the French music hall artiste, Mistinguett, took up the theme of jazz at the Casino de Paris in *Paris qui Jazze*, in which the chorus of the title song of the revue declared:

> Y a du jazz-band le jour et la nuit,
> Y a du jazz-band partout!
> C'est le grand succès de Paris
> Qui rend les hommes fous!

(There are jazz bands day and night,
There are jazz bands everywhere!
It's the big success of Paris
That drives men crazy!)

L Julsen and Harola de Bozzi

In the Twenties, the 'sweet and piercing saxophone' was considered the newest sound from across the Atlantic. Records of ragtime and Negro jazz were within everyone's reach. Dancing was the fastest-growing craze, and the gramophone and the cocktail were the symbols of the age. Much of the mood of the period was summed up in Victor Margueritte's novel, *La Garçonne*, which enjoyed a *succès de scandale* when it was published in 1922. In it the author describes people 'crazily dancing in a blue light to the wild rhythms of jazz bands…'

In fashion, the 'flapper' had replaced the girl with the hourglass figure. The new straight lines and geometric designs reflected the cubist art and decoration that could be seen at the Art Deco Exhibition. The cropped hair, long cigarette holders and green-painted fingernails were the outward signs of women's new sense of emancipation.

In the music hall, the sexes unexpectedly met in the single ambiguous personage of Barbette, an American acrobat, who drew large crowds to the Casino de Paris and whose golden curls and sequinned costume concealed the muscular body of a man.

It was against this unfamiliar background of activity that the *Revue Nègre* company from New York stepped off the boat train in Paris on a grey autumn day in 1925. None of the troupe was aware of the intense intellectual and artistic atmosphere into which they were about to be plunged. Without realising it, they were shortly to make their own unexpected contribution to that much vaunted 'new mode of living'. The *Revue Nègre* was billed to appear at the Théâtre des Champs-Élysées, a vast modern structure that had recently become Europe's biggest music hall.

La Revue Nègre

It is difficult to adequately describe the *Revue Nègre*, or to fully explain the impact it had in Paris in 1925. To bring us even a distant echo of the sights and sounds that assailed audiences at the Théâtre des Champs-Élysées that autumn one must turn to written accounts of the *Revue*. But such was the general atmosphere of excitement and suspense surrounding its presentation, one is tempted to doubt even the eyes and ears of those who were actually there.

Late in September 1925, posters appeared in the streets of Paris announcing:

> From the 2nd to the 15th October – For the first time in Paris – The Théâtre des Champs-Élysées Music Hall presents a NEGRO REVUE in 9 tableaux, produced by Caroline Dudley... with Josephine Baker and Louis Douglas...

The names of other participants followed in smaller letters and included Sydney Bechet, Maud de Forest and Joe Alex. The music was by Spencer Williams and other, unnamed, 'famous American Negro composers'.

The *Revue* was part of a fortnightly music hall programme inaugurated earlier in the year at the theatre. Few, if any, of those named in the *Revue Nègre* were known to Paris audiences. Louis Douglas, the dancer, had appeared at the Bataclan Theatre and the Creole saxophonist, Sydney Bechet, had played at the Alhambra Theatre four years before, in a revue starring Mistinguett. The names of Dudley and Baker were as unknown to Paris audiences as the rest of the coloured American troupe.

Posters appearing on the tall Morris advertisement columns also announced the appearance of the singer Saint-Granier (Jean de Cassagnac) in the same programme. This well-known French entertainer's name dominated all others in huge black letters at the foot of the poster, but he was unconnected with the *Revue Nègre*.

It was the custom for music hall programmes of the period to be divided into two parts, with popular favourites opening the bill, followed by a well-known 'star' performer who appeared just before the interval and closed the first half of the programme. The second half of the bill usually comprised a comic tableau or act with music. It was here that the *Revue Nègre* was billed to appear and to occupy the entire second half of the advertised programme for two weeks from Friday, 2 October 1925.

As in previous weeks, the music hall programme for the first half of October borrowed heavily from the circus. It included the Jenkins Brothers in their eccentric dance routine, the Alison Girls on the trampoline, the Klein Family of Acrobats, and a weightlifter named Louis Vasseur. The evening's entertainment was supported by the Champs-Élysées Girls and the regular pit orchestra conducted by Eugène Bigot.

Those who bought tickets for the Théâtre des Champs-Élysées at the beginning of October mostly did so to see Saint-Granier, the 'Grand Fantaisiste', as he was called, who had recently abandoned satirical songs for sentimental ballads, and closed his turn with his arrangements of such songs as 'Marqueta' and 'Ramona', of which he was part-author.

Audiences had been well primed by the press to expect something unusual from the *Revue Nègre*. A few days before its appearance the director of the state-run Odéon Theatre, Monsieur Firmin Gémier, offered his impressions of Negro dancing he had seen recently in New York, and wrote in the daily literary and arts newspaper, *Comoedia*: 'They will astonish you. You cannot imagine their fantasy, their lively spirit. It sparkles! They demonstrate an extraordinary originality. They hide the sun under their black skins.'

Even if they had not actually seen members of the American troupe in the city, most Parisians were aware of their arrival. From the moment they had stepped off the boat train at Saint-Lazare railway station, their bizarre appearance and incomprehensible chatter had caused widespread amusement and curiosity. Even their everyday clothes possessed a theatrical extravagance. The women wore red and white check dresses, red stockings, green shoes with red laces, and balanced floral headdresses like small gardens in their heads. The men were attired in a similarly flamboyant style with little black bowler hats, white gloves and red and white gaiters. They all walked with a rhythmic, swinging stride and expressed childish delight at everything they saw.

To offer the *Revue Nègre* the best chance of success, the management of the Théâtre des Champs-Élysées had organised a special midnight *répétition générale* or public dress rehearsal, to which an exclusive audience of influential theatre-goers had been invited.

On the day of the opening of the *Revue Nègre* the theatrical magazine *Comoedia* wrote:

> Tonight Messrs Rolf de Maré and André Daven are bravely attempting something entirely new. For the first time in Paris they are presenting an entirely Negro revue, lifted from its very sources in the Negro quarter of New York.

On behalf of the theatre, André Daven then offered his own last-minute explanation of what the public was about to see.

> We are not claiming to put on a very Parisian show, a sugary revue. You will see these twenty-five Negroes, in typical scenes and in their crude state. We haven't changed or altered anything. It might not appeal to everybody, but all the same, Negro art is really something. The greatest artists in the world have praised its ever-welling force.

The *Comoedia* reviewer then added:

> Naïve décors show hams, outsize watermelons or old paddle-steamers in a distant port. There are dancers on a skyscraper, and dazzling coloured dresses. All this jiggers about to the sound of jazz, soft one moment, then throbbing, brutal, earthy or spasmodic the next. A raging rhythm shakes all these black legs and brown arms covered with pearls; a strange sight which might offend our European eyes and ears.
>
> The troupe includes a few stars, who, though unknown in Europe, are all the rage in New York. Josephine Baker is not only a very attractive Negress, but also a dancer with a lot of life in her legs and a remarkable sense of caricature.

André Daven concluded the article with an anecdote.

> Here's an amusing detail if you like. We had the devil of a time trying to stop all these coloured artists from putting on white make-up, following the great fashion of the Negro theatre in New York.

As '*Tout Paris*' who had been invited to the Friday opening settled into their seats there was an atmosphere of suppressed excitement in the theatre. Critics and members of the artistic establishment had turned up in force. The presence of such personalities as Robert Desnos, Fernand Léger, Picabia, Van Dongen and Blaise Cendrars, indicated that something out of the ordinary was expected. After reading Daven's apology in *Comoedia* many people wanted to be there – even if the *Revue* was a total flop.

A pocket-sized programme, printed in one colour, devoted exclusively to the *Revue*, was distributed. It gave the titles of the different scenes, or tableaux, together with the names of the individual members of the troupe. A framed oval portrait photograph of Josephine Baker, with darkly rouged lips and wearing a bead necklace, adorned the inside left-hand page. The programme gave no hint of the 'fantasy' or 'force' described in the press.

As the lights of the auditorium dimmed that Friday night, a hush fell over the assembly. Eight coloured musicians, wearing red jackets and carrying their instruments, marched in single file onto the stage and took up their places in front of the pearl-grey curtains. The curtains then rose to reveal a backdrop decorated with geometric designs, and the musicians played a brief overture in a jazz idiom.

Those who studied their programme were informed that it was entitled 'Shimmy-Sha Wable' (sic). The backdrop then rose to reveal a port scene by night. On the quayside were bales, rum barrels and figures sprawled asleep. Away in the distance the lights of cargo boats and a pale moon was visible. Night was nearly over.

As morning light grew, the figures in shirts and dresses, wearing straw hats and turbans, slowly roused to sing a short song. A glance at the programme announced that it was called 'Mississippi Stem Boat-Race' (sic). The 'Charleston Steppers' then took over and launched into a full-blooded Charleston. The *Revue Nègre* was under way.

It was then there occurred one of those rare moments which makes an audience sit up and take notice. Like a wild animal released from a cage, an agile, half-clad figure leapt on to the stage from the wings.

The reviewer in *Candide* wrote:

> …a curious figure dashes on stage, sagging at the knees, wearing a pair of tattered shorts and looking like a cross between a boxing kangaroo, a piece of chewing gum and a racing cyclist – it's Josephine Baker!

Other observers seized on the simile of a kangaroo. Gérard Banër wrote:

> An extraordinary character appears, dressed in underpants, advancing with her supple knees apart, her stomach concave like a kangaroo. An agile, trilling voice escapes from this frenzied being…

Another spectator, Pierre de Régnier, also likened the apparition to a kangaroo when he wrote:

> It walks with bent knees, wearing ragged pants and resembling a boxing kangaroo… and a racing cyclist. Josephine Baker. Is it a man? Is it a woman? Her lips are painted black, her skin is banana coloured, her short hair stuck to her head, as if she were wearing caviar, her voice is extremely high-pitched and agitated by a perpetual trembling, her body wriggles like that of a snake or, more precisely, it appears to be a moving saxophone, and the sounds of the orchestra seem to issue from inside herself; she is grimacing and bruised, she squints, she puffs out her cheeks; disarticulates herself, does the splits and, finally, goes off on all fours, with her legs stiff and her backside higher than her head, like a very young giraffe.
>
> Is she horrible, is she ravishing, is she a Negro, is she white, has she any hair or is her skull painted black? Nobody knows. There isn't time to find out. She returns just as she left, as quick as a one-step tune; it isn't a woman, it isn't a dancer, it's something extravagant and fugitive like the music, the ectoplasm in a sense of all the sounds we hear.

Paul Colin, the theatre's scene painter, who had been accustomed since April to seeing eccentric and exotic performers, was carried away by Josephine's animal presence. He recalled:

> She was a cross between a boxing kangaroo, an India rubber woman and Tarzan's woman. She contorted her body, squinted, shook herself about and blew up her cheeks as she crossed the stage on all fours.

After Josephine's frenzied appearance, a change of mood was offered when the curtain rose on a vast empty stage dominated by decor representing New York skyscrapers. The audience heard the plaintive sound of a single clarinet being played and Sydney Bechet emerged dressed as a street trader, pushing a multicoloured barrow of vegetables with one hand and playing a melancholy tune with the other. The vibrant, soaring notes possessed all the pain and sorrow of 'Big City Blues'. The applause that accompanied him was almost as great as that which had greeted Josephine.

Few accounts equalled the visual imagery of correspondent Janet Flanner's report in the *New Yorker* magazine, when she described Josephine's first appearance with her partner, Joe Alex, later that night:

> She made her entry entirely nude, except for a pink flamingo feather between her limbs; she was being carried upside down and doing the splits on the shoulders of a black giant. Mid-stage he paused and, with his long fingers holding her basket-wise around the waist, swung her in a slow cartwheel to the stage floor, where she stood like his magnificent discarded burden, in a moment of complete silence. She was an unforgettable female ebony statue. A roar of approval spread through the theatre.
>
> Whatever happened next was unimportant. The two specific elements had been established and were unforgettable – her magnificent dark body, a new model that to the French proved for the first time that black was beautiful, and the acute response of the white masculine public in the capital of hedonism of all Europe – Paris.

The *Revue Nègre* lasted about three-quarters of an hour, the tableaux loosely linked together with music and dance performed jointly by the twenty-five dancers and musicians. As each sequence unfolded to the insistent rhythms of Negro jazz, it slowly became apparent to the audience that this was '*Un Événement*', something to be talked about and that the young black dancer was the latest sensation on the Paris music hall stage.

The *Revue Nègre* ended with a nightclub scene in which Josephine and the other girls danced in a way that many found suggestive, not to say lewd. Josephine appeared completely naked except for a little girdle of red and green feathers around her hips and another around her neck. As Paul Colin recalled, 'Naked, with just a garland of green feathers around her hips and with her skull lacquered black, she provoked anger and enthusiasm.'

Pierre de Régnier called the dance 'barbaric' and wrote:

This dance of rare impropriety is the triumph of lewdness, the return to the practices of the early ages: the declaration of love made in silence with the arms above the head, with a simple forward movement of the abdomen, and the whole rear quivering...

Feathers flutter in time and their fluttering is cleverly calculated... Josephine swirling around in her feathers, the girls bawl out and the curtain falls to a tremendous roll of the drums and a final clash of cymbals.

Josephine's costume, or lack of it, had undoubtedly contributed to the sensuality of the dance. When the final curtain fell an explosion of ecstatic applause swept the hall. Not since the appearance of the Russian Ballet in 1913 had the theatre been the scene of such turmoil. Josephine Baker and the *Revue Nègre* had scored a triumph.

Janet Flanner in the *New Yorker* summed up the general feeling of elation that Josephine's appearance had produced:

Within a half-hour of the final curtain on opening night, the news and meaning of her arrival had spread by the grapevine up to the cafés on the Champs-Élysées, where witnesses of her triumph sat over their drinks excitedly repeating their report of what they had just seen...

The *Revue Nègre* delighted and shocked successive Paris audiences. Its run was extended beyond the originally advertised fortnight, and new posters were printed announcing the extension.

An illustrated poster signed by Paul Colin made its appearance during the following days. It showed two Negro heads with rolling eyes, and a Negress with angular limbs, hands on hips in a provocative pose. Few doubted that the female figure was inspired by Josephine Baker. The poster, in an aggressively modern style, attracted still more people to the *Revue Nègre*.

Those who returned a second and a third time to see the *Revue Nègre* observed that changes had been introduced in the sequence of the tableaux. Two additional musical numbers had been added: a West Indian dancer named Mathilde Darlin (later to become known as Baby Darling) had joined the troupe, and the chorus line performed a tom-tom dance dressed in near transparent white robes. To whet the appetite and heighten anticipation during the interval, 'Dudley's Famous Jazz Band', in reality the Claude Hopkins group, played in the entrance hall as a prelude to the *Revue*. The Champs-Élysées Girls, who had hitherto provided continuity between the turns, disappeared entirely from the programme.

The *Revue Nègre* was now preceded by such music hall turns as 'Ruth Budd – the Girl with the Smile', Pierre Pradier doing his imitations, 'Gavroche' singing 'Loulou de Poméranie', and an artiste at the height of her powers, the great Damia. It was, however, Josephine whom most people crowded to see at the Théâtre des Champs-Élysées during October. Everywhere in Paris the same question was asked: 'Have you seen the black girl who dances in the *Revue Nègre*?'

Not all critics, however, accepted the *Revue* on its terms or were beguiled by Josephine's charms. A reviewer writing in *Candide* began his article on Josephine:

> Much has been written about her. People have gone back to see her a second, even a sixth time. Others have left their seats after two numbers, stumped out of the theatre, slamming the doors and calling it a disgrace, madness, anarchy and pandering to the baser instincts...

Critics such as Frajaville, Legrand-Chabrier, Maurice Verne and Louis Léon-Martin joined in the chorus of judgement of the *Revue Nègre*, and René Bizet, the grandson of the composer of *Carmen* wrote disparagingly in *Candide*, 'This Negro folklore is only tolerable when adapted by the intelligence of whites.' The sharpest condemnation of Josephine came from Monsieur Harmel, who wrote in *La Rumeur*, 'By the indecency of your body you dishonour the French music hall.'

The *Revue Nègre* managed to provoke extremes of opinion until it closed in mid-November. Writing in *Le Figaro* under the headline 'Obscenity', Robert de Flers took a violent stand against both the theatre and the revue. In a model of reactionary criticism he characterised the revue as 'lamentable transatlantic exhibitionism' and expressed his 'anger and shame' at the offence offered to French taste that 'takes us back to the apes quicker than we have descended from them'.

The *Revue Nègre* closed on Sunday 15 November and, still elated by the reception they had received, the company left to perform in Berlin. During the six weeks in Paris, the company had become the talk of the town and the newly discovered personality in their midst had been launched upon a career over whose course, for the moment, she had little control. If she never again appeared in public, Josephine would be remembered as the lithe half-caste beauty who danced like a wild creature and who also possessed the grace of a panther.

Writers and critics had been outspoken in praise or condemnation of the revue and prominent members of the intellectual establishment had returned again to savour the delights offered in the *Revue Nègre*. Despite the reserve of those who were afraid they'd be offended, few could resist going to see what all the fuss was about.

But even without the finely tuned praise of critics and intellectuals, Josephine and her fellow artists possessed a basic popular appeal to which the public readily responded. Without trying to explain it, they simply enjoyed its refreshingly unfamiliar rhythms and revelled in what appeared to be a return to basic emotions expressed through black American music and dance.

With a minimum of means, the *Revue Nègre* had struck a blow for freedom of expression far beyond the modest limits envisaged by its producers. In practical terms, the troupe was credited with bringing the Charleston to Paris and helping to popularise the dance in Europe. But most of all, the *Revue Nègre* served to reveal a new young dancer who had unexpectedly sprung into prominence.

The *Revue* came and went like a hurricane, leaving no one who saw it unmoved. In a profession in which indifference spells failure, the show had made its mark. But for all the stir it caused, no one filmed any part of it or recorded any of its music and songs. The few existing photographs of the troupe show only static figures against a sombre background and suggest none of the erratic action or striking clothes that so astonished Parisians.

Today the *Revue Nègre* exists only in theatrical archives and Paul Colin's poster depicting Josephine, hands on her hips in an angular, provocative pose, with two Negro heads with rolling eyes in the foreground. Colin's poster of Josephine marked the beginning of his career as theatrical designer; together they had captured the spirit of 'Les Années Folles' and Paris of the Twenties.

Despite her poor understanding of French, Josephine was aware, from her perusal of the newspapers and the behaviour of those around her, that alone among her fellow artists she had been singled out for special attention. Many had admired Sydney Bechet's saxophone and clarinet playing, and Maud de Forest's singing of the blues. But most critics focused on Josephine, whose performance, even if they did not like it, challenged their descriptive abilities.

Owing to her own inexperience and the swiftness of events that had brought her to prominence, Josephine was unable to appreciate the true value of the furore that her appearance had unleashed. The unfolding of events was enough to turn the head of any newly arrived nineteen-year-old in Paris. She simply allowed herself to be carried forward like a surfer on the crest of a wave. As she was later to affirm, 'Paris adopted me from the very first evening. I understood and am passionately in love with Paris.'

Although she was ill prepared to give any serious thought to her immediate future, this was already being done for her. Almost literally waiting in the wings were those ready and eager to take her affairs in hand, to seek to exploit and extend her talents.

One impresario who was more astute than others and sure of his judgement invited Josephine to be his leading lady in Paris the following year. Paul Derval of the Folies Bergère offered Josephine an immediate contract for his second production to go into rehearsal after Christmas. Without realising the implications or questioning her legal right to do so, Josephine signed and took a decisive step in her career. But before she could descend the famous staircase on the stage of the Folies she would be obliged to climb the stone steps of the Palais de Justice to answer a summons for breach of contract suit brought by her American sponsor, Caroline Dudley.

Berlin

Berlin received the *Revue Nègre* with even more enthusiasm than Paris had done. News of its success and of Josephine's triumph had already reached the German capital and audiences were anxious to test their judgement against that of the Parisians. The fact that the revue was presented in the Nelson Theatre, a much smaller hall than the Théâtre des Champs-Élysées, only increased the determination of those clamouring for admission to get a glimpse of the much talked-about 'Black Venus'.

They were not disappointed. From the very first night the critics led the field, describing Josephine as a 'figure of contemporary expressionism' and of 'German positivism'. But it mattered not what the critics wrote. Berliners adored Josephine's innocent, outgoing manner and amazing vitality on stage. Admirers showered her with gifts and prospective suitors sent her letters of ardent affection. Josephine, for her part, was enchanted with Berlin and its demonstrative inhabitants.

As the nightly rounds of pleasure lengthened into the early hours after her evening performances, thoughts of Paris began to fade. If Paris was already Josephine's first love, she had become infatuated with Berlin, a city she found vibrant with music and animation. When she entered a restaurant the band would pause and the musicians would rise to their feet to greet her. Waiters would rush to seat her, and young men – and many not so young

– would click their heels and bow in her direction.

On her way back to her hotel in the early hours the vast cafés in the brightly lit streets appeared to Josephine like giant ocean liners powered by tireless orchestras. At the hotel, scores of messages awaited her; flowers from unknown admirers, a fur coat from a rich merchant, jewellery from Baron X, the offer of an automobile; and, mysteriously, a set of six Chinese lacquered chairs... Simply by being herself and doing what she most enjoyed, which was dancing, Josephine had tapped a cornucopia of riches and adulation.

A black dance troupe led by a wild and sensual performer such as Josephine could not long escape the notice of connoisseurs of new theatrical talent. The celebrated Austrian actor-manager and producer, Max Reinhardt, who had made Berlin his home, came to see the *Revue Nègre*. He was so impressed by Josephine's stage presence that he immediately offered to train her to become a dramatic actress. Reinhardt proposed that she abandon the music hall and study under him for three years at his drama school at the Deutsches Theater.

Reinhardt's offer was beyond Josephine's comprehension, coming as it did from someone whose professional reputation was completely unknown to her. She had learned to treat similar sounding proposals with no more than smiles and promises. The temporary attentions of less demanding admirers were more interesting, and profitable, to her than projects offering uncertain long-term returns. The present tour of the *Revue Nègre* was a resounding success and she saw no good reason to make a change. Having made his offer, Reinhardt retreated and left Josephine to her seemingly endless round of rendezvous and receptions.

An unexpected arrival in Berlin brought Josephine abruptly down to earth. A special envoy of Paul Derval of the Folies Bergère, Mr Lorett, suddenly presented himself at Josephine's dressing room. He demanded to know when she was returning to Paris to begin rehearsals for the revue for which she had been engaged. Had she forgotten her contractual obligations? he asked.

The truth was that not only had Josephine allowed the contract to be pushed from her mind, she had also neglected to tell Caroline Dudley, her sponsor, or anyone else in the *Revue*

Nègre company, that she had agreed to join the Folies Bergère in the coming year. Josephine hesitated. She was beginning to sense her rising value in the eyes of producers. On the one hand there was her commitment to Caroline Dudley and the *Revue Nègre*. On the other hand she was being held to a contract she had made with Paul Derval of the Folies Bergère. And in the midst of her discovery of Berlin, the great Reinhardt had offered to make her a 'great dramatic actress'. The moment had come to take a further decisive step in her career and raise the stakes.

Anxiously waiting in Paris for news of his new leading artiste, Paul Derval suddenly received a telegram from Josephine demanding a bonus of four hundred francs a performance to be added to her contract before she returned to Paris. The ultimatum shocked him. Plans were already well advanced for the new revue which revolved largely around the personality of Josephine. Songs, scenes and scenarios were being prepared to exploit her exotic appeal to the maximum. After calculating the risk of losing her altogether and sustaining enormous losses in money and prestige if he refused her demand, Derval capitulated and sent a message back to Berlin, 'All right, but return immediately.'

The *Revue Nègre* troupe from which Josephine had sprung was informed of her departure. They all knew that it could not continue without her. There were tearful farewells at the Nelson Theatre. Sydney Bechet and members of the Louis Mitchell's Jazz Kings prepared to leave for Moscow, where they had work. Others were offered their train and boat tickets back to Paris and New York.

Josephine packed her trunks and, together with those gifts she could conveniently carry, boarded the train for Paris. The *Revue Nègre* company was no more, but it would be remembered as one of the strangest success stories in music hall history. Exactly how that success had been achieved, and who was really responsible for Josephine's leap to fame, would only come to light in later years.

Justice, Josephine and Robeson

When Josephine first signed a contract with Paul Derval to appear at the Folies Bergère in Paris, it marked a break with her original sponsor, Caroline Dudley. Not only had Josephine accepted a better offer to appear in Paris, she had even negotiated from Berlin a higher fee than that first agreed to with Derval, and she was abandoning the *Revue Nègre*, all without consideration for Dudley who had brought her to Europe.

For her part, Dudley was angry and aggrieved at Josephine's apparent indifference and ingratitude. She and her sisters had spent a great deal of time and effort in launching the revue from New York. Josephine's defection meant the loss of a financial investment for Dudley and her husband, who had paid the bills. Dudley took the only course open to her; she decided to take Josephine to court to sue her for 200,000 francs damages for breach of contract. She had been receiving $1000 a month from Josephine.

Both Josephine and Dudley were Americans abroad. While Josephine had become adept in bargaining for the terms of her engagement, without the help of an agent, Dudley, as the wife of a Foreign Service officer, had free access to legal advice. But theatrical litigation could be lengthy and costly and neither party had any experience in such matters.

Fifty years after the event I searched out Caroline Dudley, still living in France, to learn more about the difference that had arisen between Josephine and her mentor. The widow of her second husband, the French writer Joseph Delteil (celebrated for having scripted Carl Dreyer's film *La Passion de Jeanne d'Arc*), she was living in a large ramshackle country house surrounded by cactuses and vines, on the edge of wild heath land near Montpellier in south-west France.

I asked Madame Caroline Delteil, by now well into her seventies, about her relations with Josephine all those years ago. 'It's all buried in my subconscious,' she replied. 'You're digging it all out! The fact was, everyone wanted her.' Was she sorry Josephine had signed for the Folies Bergère, I asked. 'Oh, yes! I told her, you're doing harm to your soul. And Josephine replied, "Madame, I'm feeling fine!" I don't think she knew she had a soul!'

When I reminded her of the lawsuit, the memory of it came back clearly to her.

'I went up the steps of the Court House – the Palais de Justice

– in Paris, and there was Josephine going up the other side. This was not a bit my style. And I said, "Oh, Josephine, let's stop the whole thing. I can't stand any of this nonsense. You're perfectly free!"' After a moment's reflection Madame Delteil added, 'I was sorry not to have done a second show with her. It might have been wonderful.'

It was not the end of the affair for Caroline Dudley. Encouraged by her apparent flair for bringing black music and dance to France, she cast around for another coloured personality to head a new show. Her choice fell on an earlier member of *Shuffle Along* in New York, who had since made a name for himself in both New York and London... Paul Robeson. She recalled it clearly.

'I was in London with my sister,' she remembered. 'We heard about *Show Boat* on the radio. I loved Robeson's singing. I've always loved it.' She broke off to huskily sing a few notes of 'Ole' Man River'. 'I wanted Robeson for another show. I hadn't had enough! I wanted to put on a super *Revue Nègre* with Robeson. He made a contract with me to do it.'

(Paul Robeson had pursued a parallel course to Josephine. After a brief appearance in *Shuffle Along*, he took over the leading role in Eugene O'Neill's play *The Emperor Jones*, followed by the first stage version of *Show Boat*, a musical comedy based on Edna Ferber's novel of miscegenation on the Mississippi. Robeson's towering presence and magnificent voice launched him on an international career in films and theatre.)

Madame Delteil then related how she entered into a second legal battle.

'Robeson was having such a success in London with *Show Boat* that the contract he had just signed went to hell. He signed and then he had to pay me. I'd started a lawsuit against Robeson and the Drury Lane Theatre. I had to defend myself. Mr Justice Maugham said it was a case for heavy damages. Robeson was told he could never sing again unless he made good Dudley's damages. That cheered me up. At least I was going to get heavy damages.'

The end of Caroline Dudley's foray into show business came in the post.

'I had a pile of letters that I'd never opened. Finally I opened one and in it was a cheque – I've forgotten for how much. Oh, a big sum! And so he made good my damages, or he could not have continued singing. I never did a show again. And then I married Joseph Delteil and that was another show! That was almost as difficult as thirty-five Negroes!'

Chapter Two
The Truth about *La Revue Nègre*

The advent of the *Revue Nègre* is considered a landmark in French music hall history, and its impact and importance have been compared to that of the Russian Ballet in Paris sixteen years earlier. Both events provoked violent and conflicting reactions, and both are credited with crystallising the mood and the spirit of their respective periods. A more apt comparison could perhaps be made with the carnival atmosphere surrounding the first performance of Eric Satie's fantasy ballet, *Parade*, in 1917. His innovative use of circus, music hall and jazz motifs set the tone for the post-war years and truly heralded the period of 'Les Années Folles', the Crazy Years.

Whatever parallels may be found with other theatrical events, Josephine Baker and the *Revue Nègre* are now firmly planted in the annals of the Twenties and stand on their own merits. It is somewhat surprising, therefore, to learn that at the very last moment the *Revue* was nearly not put on at all, and at one point during rehearsals Josephine was ready to return to New York whence she had come only days before.

The success of the *Revue Nègre* was all the more remarkable for the apparent amateurishness with which it was conceived, assembled and shipped to France. The exercise involved a group who were, to say the least, mostly unacquainted with the vagaries of popular French 'boulevard' entertainment. They included a former Swedish industrialist turned impresario, an American society woman, a young French producer who aspired to put on Grandes Revues, and a jobless painter who had only once been in a theatre before he was landed with the task of scene painting and poster designing. The most curious aspect of the whole affair was the major contribution by an outside 'entrepreneur' which no one, afterwards, wanted to acknowledge.

Who first discovered Josephine Baker and how she did emerge from a motley group of black dancers and musicians to become, overnight, one of the brightest stars of the Twenties? It was not until years later that claims were laid for having chosen and promoted Josephine from among the group of anonymous dancers, and for having saved from disaster a troupe lacking an effective producer or star performer. None of the first-night audience or subsequent audiences were aware of the degree of doubt and confusion that reigned (even in such a notoriously precarious operation) before the curtain rose on the first night, or that the audacious appearance of Josephine with her dance partner was the result of a last-minute improvisation by an outside hand. Few of those closely involved agreed afterwards how this had been accomplished. Indeed, none cared after Josephine had made her triumphant debut. The only thing that mattered was that 'The "Black Venus" has arrived!' The surviving members of the company never ceased to dispute the issue of Josephine's emergence and the historic success of the *Revue Nègre*.

Dudley in Harlem

The idea of presenting a group of black American artistes in their own show in Paris is claimed by Caroline Dudley, the daughter of an American senator from Chicago and wife to an American Foreign Service officer. While living in New York in the early 1920s, she and her sisters frequented Harlem. 'We went to Harlem every day, practically lived there,' she recalls. 'I always liked the way the blacks moved. You saw them walking about the streets or singing. I had friends there…'

Caroline Dudley conceived the idea of exporting a troupe of black dancers and musicians to Paris, where she believed they would be well received, and began visiting theatres and clubs to audition performers.

'I can't imagine what gave me the idea. The devil, I think! It just came into my head. I couldn't get rid of it. Our house in New York was like a sweatshop because we were making costumes right and left.'

Caroline Dudley not only toured New York looking for talent but also outlying districts of the city. The black jazz pianist,

Claude Hopkins, remembers she came to hear his band play at an establishment called the Smile Awhile Café in Ashbury, in the neighbouring state of New Jersey. When Hopkins learned that she was recruiting performers for a European tour, he played several comedy numbers for her benefit. The band was offered a contract on the spot and a week later they joined others in New York who were already rehearsing for the tour.

Among the artists Caroline Dudley engaged to dance the Charleston in Paris was a light-skinned Negress named Josephine, whom she saw in the chorus line at the fashionable Plantation Club. Josephine stood out because of her clowning as 'end-girl' and Dudley persuaded her to join those already hired.

Casting her mind back more than half a century, Caroline Dudley recalls the formalities of Josephine's departure from New York for Paris.

'My, but she was pretty! When they asked her at the passport office if she was married or divorced, all she could answer in that nasal voice was, "Yes… no! Yes… no!"'

Dudley remembers that Josephine vaguely mentioned an earlier marriage. 'She wasn't very pleased. She wasn't very proud of it.' (The truth was that Josephine was still legally married to her second black American husband. Her two marriages to blacks in America would remain concealed until many years later.)

Whatever she suspected, Dudley did nothing to deter Josephine from leaving the country and seeking a new life abroad. She used her diplomatic connections and offered to act as guardian to her protégée for the necessary formalities.

'Because she was entirely uneducated, unable to write her own name, she made a cross on the passport,' says Dudley. The newly formed company embarked on the *Berengaria* for Europe on 15 September 1925.

Josephine was something of a handful on the boat. Overexcited at the prospect of performing in Paris, she insisted, against Caroline Dudley's advice, in trying to sing at the concert that they were invited to give for the passengers in first class. Her independent nature had already been noted before they sailed, Caroline Dudley remembers.

'Even in New York Josephine had wanted to sing pretty little

39

sweet, white, Mistinguett-type songs. I kept her away from rehearsals where Clara Smith, a marvellous voice, and Ethel Waters were singing because I didn't dare for her to see them. She was wonderful, a marvellous clown. And I said, "Never forget it, Josephine. You're very beautiful, and you know how to dance, and you're a clown, and don't forget it!"'

Disregarding this advice Josephine chose to attempt to sing two sentimental ballads, 'Brown Eyes' and 'If you hadn't gone away', at the ship's concert. The result was a disaster. She was off-key and out of step with the orchestra and collapsed in tears of humiliation, crying that she wanted to return to New York immediately. Comforted by Caroline Dudley and Sydney Bechet, ('the only one who didn't make fun of me when I sang "Brown Eyes"'), she agreed to take a look at Paris before returning home. They were already halfway across the Atlantic.

Harlem Comes to Paris

The arrival of the *Revue Nègre* could not have come at a better time for the management of the Champs-Élysées Theatre. Because of its size and location, the theatre had a reputation for being unlucky, a difficult house to fill, and something of a white elephant.

Situated on the dignified Avenue Montaigne, half a mile away from the famous Avenue des Champs-Élysées, the huge theatre had been built in 1913 as an opera and concert hall, but it stood in a quiet, badly lit quarter with poor means of communication. Its creator and first administrator, Gabriel Astruc, presented Diaghilev's Russian Ballet during the theatre's inaugural season, but he ran into debt and the theatre was forced to close its doors.

It was not until 1920 that Jacques Hébertot, the new administrator, reopened the theatre and attempted to revive its aim of becoming a 'temple of opera and classical dance'. A Swedish industrialist, Rolf de Maré, financed a series of classical concerts, French and Russian drama, and his pet interest, the Swedish Ballet.

De Maré saw himself as in impresario in the Diaghilev mould, but his favoured protégé, a dancer, Jean Borlin, was not another Nijinsky. Wagging tongues forecast that the theatre would ruin

Hébertot as it had Astruc. After various economy measures designed to cover falling receipts, Hébertot pulled out, relinquishing his lease to de Maré who took on a young French associate, André Daven, to help him revive the theatre's fortunes.

In the spring of 1925, de Maré and Daven decided on a radical change of policy and inaugurated what they called a 'New Paris Music Hall' with a complete change of programme every two weeks. In boldly lettered posters the management promised to present the 'most extraordinary, athletic, acrobatic, and comic attractions', most of which would be appearing in Paris for the first time. In deference to the theatre's supposed reputation for serious musical entertainment, the management also promised to present 'actors, great poets and musicians…' on the same bill as 'dancers and illusionists and the most eccentric music hall and circus turns'. A large orchestra would assure the continuity of the programmes. The public could hardly ask for more.

When everything was ready, de Maré said to Daven, 'We'll continue through the spring and if the public doesn't show up we'll close the doors.'

From the theatre's inauguration in April, a veritable galaxy of known and unknown names appeared on the playbills, including such personalities as Max Déarly, Willemetz, Harry Pilcer, Loie Fuller, Pavlova, and Colette. When the management was offered a Negro revue from America, they accepted, believing it could not fail to find its place in such a wide and all-embracing spectrum of entertainment. It would even attract visitors from the nearby Decorative Arts Exhibition. There was only one small problem. Until the company of black artistes assembled on the stage of the Paris theatre for the first rehearsal, no one had any idea what form the so-called revue would take, and no one had ever seen them perform together as a troupe.

Paul Colin

It is here that there begins to be a divergence of opinion over what happened next. Paul Colin, who was the theatre's scene painter at the time and had the task of producing a poster to advertise the revue, claims that it was he who first pointed out Josephine's qualities to the management of the theatre when they were first confronted by the group of completely unknown performers.

In his eighty-seventh year, the celebrated French designer recalled how his illustrated poster for the *Revue Nègre* contributed to Josephine's promotion in Paris and helped launch him on a successful career as a stage and publicity designer.

'I was engaged at the time when a rich Swedish industrialist, Rolf de Maré, had taken the theatre to present a young dancer, Jean Borlin. Having the lease of the theatre, he had organised a music hall with his associate, André Daven. They put on some big shows... Chinese gladiators, Spanish and African dancers, jazz bands, dance troupes from the South of France and all kinds of classical dancers. Every day there were new leading artistes...

'One day an American woman suggested to de Maré to take her *Revue Nègre*. The troupe arrived at Saint-Lazare railway station at ten in the morning, and after having been taken to their specially reserved hotel, they were at the theatre by eleven.

'I can see them still,' recalled Colin half a century later. 'They took my breath away... The star of the troupe was Maud de Forest, a woman with a beautiful voice – but enormous!

'I had the time to see the troupe for two or three hours of rehearsal to get inspiration from them because I had to do a poster. I had never tried to do Negro designs. I didn't know that kind of American. They bore no resemblance to our West Africans, and my only knowledge of these blacks came from spirituals, which I found interesting; but that wasn't enough on which to base a poster. The only way to do my poster was to find a Negro and a Negress among the twenty artistes to interpret the Harlem style.

'I looked for a pretty girl among the fifteen or so women and I found one, far prettier than the others, and different, with, above all, a beautiful body. Her head was the same as many Negresses, good but not extraordinary. With make-up, one can make a good-looking woman very beautiful, but one cannot change the breasts and one cannot change the legs. Well, I looked for a girl like that and I chose one and she was called Josephine.

'The troupe arrived at ten in the morning, and at ten in the evening, Josephine, in all her perfection, was posing nude in my studio. She took up Negro poses, I made sketches and from them

I made my poster.'

Paul Colin then reached the point of his story where he lamented that it was not Josephine who was the star of the revue.

'The day after Josephine's visit to my studio I remarked to the management, "It's a pity not to have a pretty girl like that as the star. The leading lady is plump and Parisians don't like that, even if she sings well."

'Daven echoed my feeling and de Maré immediately gave orders that Josephine be given prominence over Maud de Forest. The plump Negress said nothing and retreated into the background. They worked on Josephine for fifteen days. She was naturally very proud and happy to have the lead.

'The evening of the première they held a big party with champagne and caviar for the whole theatre. The next morning the Parisian press was unanimous: "The 'Black Venus' has arrived!" It was the real beginning of Josephine Baker.'

Paul Colin also readily admits it was also the beginning for him. 'The day I designed the poster for the *Revue Nègre* I had captured, I don't know how, the art of Harlem, an art which has its own character, its own particular nature and very different roots from ours. Since that day, and that poster, I had great success and many clients.'

Thus ends the substance of Paul Colin's version of how Josephine came to be selected as a solo performer from amongst more than twenty-five anonymous coloured performers.

Jacques-Charles

A quite different version of Josephine's leap to stardom is told by Jacques-Charles, who was working at another theatre at the time. He tells a story of confusion and panic between the time the troupe arrived at the theatre and the first night of the *Revue Nègre*, and claims to have played a decisive role in saving the *Revue* and launching Josephine's career.

When Rolf de Maré and his partner, André Daven, seated in the stalls of their theatre, were confronted with the apparently uncontrollable antics of a motley group of black musicians and dancers, their anticipation turned to dismay. Used to auditioning single artistes, or smaller groups, the twenty-five cavorting

Negroes in multicoloured outfits were just too much for them. Aghast at the clamour and confusion, they rapidly decided that the public would not put up with so much tap-dancing and would walk out of the theatre.

In desperation de Maré and Daven decided to call upon Jacques-Charles, the director of the Moulin Rouge and a well-known Maître de Revue, to come and advise them whether they should cancel the engagement forthwith and cut their losses, or try to save something from what they considered to be a fiasco.

Here is how Jacques-Charles remembers the crucial days of rehearsal.

'One morning about nine o'clock when I was already at work, André Daven forced his way into my office at the Moulin Rouge. He had come to call for my help! He had engaged a troupe of Negroes without having seen them, on the sole recommendation of an impresario who had announced a revue. The troupe had arrived from New York to open in a few days' time and the first rehearsal of this so-called revue caused the dismay of Daven and of Rolf de Maré. "My dear fellow, they tap-dance for two hours! They'll send everyone away! You're the only one who can save us!" said Daven.

'I protested that I had too much work and that my contract with the Moulin Rouge theatre forbade me any outside collaboration. But Daven was so insistent that I put on my overcoat and followed him to the theatre where the rehearsal was due to take place at ten o'clock. At the theatre I still expressed my doubts when Rolf de Maré joined us to say, "You must save us. Ask what you want!"

'"It's not a question of that," I replied, "but to find out if one can make something of the existing elements in forty-eight hours. First I will see what they do, and afterwards I'll tell you if you can announce your Negro troupe or cancel their contract."

'On stage, I found several coloured ladies and gentlemen all looking miserable, for they understood the management's lack of enthusiasm for their talents. Luckily their leader was a mulatto dancer, Louis Douglas, whom I had known for many years and who knew me well. I explained the situation to him. "You have two alternatives. Either you make your debut, or you take the boat home. Choose! I ask complete obedience from everyone. It's your only chance."

'After a short discussion, Douglas came to me to say that they put themselves in my hands. "Then show me everything you can do," I replied. And the rehearsal began.

'I must say that after the defeatist remarks of Daven and de Maré I was agreeably surprised. It is true that there was too much tap-dancing, which was impossibly monotonous, but there were some excellent elements in the troupe, and their talents, if well presented, could trigger success. So I reassured the troupe of coloured artistes with whom I made a rendezvous that afternoon and went off to raise the broken spirits of the two directors.

'"No! You really think so!" they exclaimed. "Well, if you say so! Let's wait till tomorrow. Really! We can make the announcement?" I left them a little more assured but still very anxious.

'The whole day was spent in pruning, trimming, altering the order of the acts, and trying to make a revue out of it all. Everyone fell in with the best goodwill and with exceptional understanding. That night I had the costumes and the decor shown to me; these had also given Daven and de Maré shivers. Of course, if one wanted to compare this material with that of the Moulin Rouge or the Casino de Paris, the comparison wasn't at all to the advantage of these poor costumes and curtains, made without taste and with poor quality materials by a small supplier in the Negro quarter of New York.

'The worst thing was that it was all so pretentious... But I knew what had to be done, because, thanks to my friend Irving Berlin, I had seen all the Negro cabarets of New York and Atlantic City and knew perfectly well the type of shows presented there. The mistake was to have wanted to look Parisian! It should look Negro!

'I mixed everything together, giving them Louis XV three-cornered hats to wear with overalls and big straw hats to wear with fur costumes. I did the same with the decor, merging the main elements of one with the backcloth of the other. The following day I lit the whole thing with strange multicoloured lighting. I was beginning to be pleased, but Daven and de Maré were still worried...

'What was still missing, however, was a slightly sensual note as a break from the jazz and tap-dancing. I spoke to Joe Alex, a mulatto I knew to be a good carrier. He assured me that one of his colleagues was ready to perform such a number with him: Josephine Baker.

'I had already noticed Josephine Baker because of the sculptural form of her figure, which her light rehearsal costume did not quite succeed in concealing.

'Josephine Baker indignantly rejected my "suggestions" for a number in which she and Alex, almost naked, would perform a wild dance – half shimmy, half poipoi – a Hawaiian and South African mixture with a touch of New Zealand. It was in vain that I left Alex the task of convincing her. When I came back, Josephine Baker was in tears and shouting she wanted to take the boat back home.

'"All right," I told her, "you can take the boat home... but *after* the opening. In the meantime you are going to do what I ask. And I called Douglas to remind him that everyone had promised, through him, to obey me without question. Josephine had to submit and she began to work over her number with Joe Alex while sniffing back tears.

'The next day, at the première, the audience raved at the dance number of Joe Alex and Josephine, dressed only in a loincloth of leaves. "Well!" I said to Rolf de Maré, "are you still worried?" My question was unnecessary. His face was shining in triumph.

'That was the start of Josephine Baker in Paris. It took so little to persuade her not to take the boat back home without ever appearing. It would have been a shame if she had.'

Jacques-Charles's account of the behind-the-scenes problems of the *Revue Nègre* appeared in the Paris press in June 1932 barely seven years after the event, when Josephine had already become a star at the Casino de Paris. As a producer with eight revues in four years to his credit, four of them with Mistinguett, before the arrival of Josephine on the Paris scene, Jacques-Charles and his account of his participation in the presentation of the *Revue Nègre* cannot be underestimated. His unsuccessful attempt to book an operetta played entirely by a black American cast in 1912 testifies to his belief in their quality as artistes. His standing as a producer on both sides of the Atlantic helps give credence to his claim to have been the *mécène* behind the success of the *Revue Nègre*. But his contribution has curiously remained unacknowledged by others, with one exception, and for that, he was to wait another eighteen years.

Jacques-Charles ended his published account with a mild reproach to the co-directors of the Champs-Élysées Theatre. '"You are saving our lives… You can ask anything you want…" they told me. I am still waiting for a simple letter of thanks! Theatre directors quickly become very forgetful when they are no longer worried. As for Josephine, she could have sent me her photograph in that costume she didn't want to wear – and has never given up since!'

Thus ends Jacques-Charles's account of the creation of the *Revue Nègre*. He was to return to the subject in 1950, when he laments that, due to their commitments abroad, Josephine and he were destined not to meet during their long careers after Josephine's debut. He then tells of their poignant meeting in the South of France.

'During a radio song festival for which I was responsible, we finally met in Nice. Timidly, Josephine approached me and asked, "Monsieur Jacques-Charles, I want to ask you something, but I am ashamed. Was it your father who put on the *Revue Nègre*?"

'I replied, "But my dear Josephine, it was me!" I saw with astonishment large tears roll down her cheeks. "Why are you crying?" I asked. "Because I was ungrateful," she replied. "I never thanked you and I owe you my entire career!" And it was my turn to be moved. Her reputation as a trouper remained intact.'

Josephine has made no reference to this incident and the veteran producer's encounter with Josephine remains uncorroborated by any other source.

Claude Hopkins and Sydney Bechet

There were omissions and anomalies in the published presentation of the revue that reflected the management's confusion over who was who during the swapping of roles backstage.

The first posters that appeared on the walls and the Morris advertisement columns in Paris listed the duration of the revue as a fortnight from 3 to 15 October. After its success the management lost no time in producing new posters, signed by Paul Colin, extending the run.

Louis Douglas now appeared as 'Deputy Administrator' of the revue, and Miguel Covarrubias, the artist, was joined by the 'Dudley Sisters' to be credited with stage decoration. Spencer Williams was joined by Jack Palmer as provider of music, but Claude Hopkins, nominal leader of the group, which included Sydney Bechet, received no credit at all on the publicity material. Neither did Maud de Forest, the demoted blues singer, who had been eclipsed by Josephine Baker. Dudley's famous Jazz Band, which played in the foyer in the interval preceding the *Revue Nègre*, was in fact the Claude Hopkins group of eight musicians with Sydney Bechet.

An unnamed producer had warned the management of the Champs-Élysées Theatre not to engage Bechet because of a drinking problem that sometimes led him into trouble. Bechet had had to leave England five years earlier after an incident while he was performing at the Alhambra Theatre in a revue starring Mistinguett. He had returned to America and toured the country before landing up again in New York where he recorded with the Clarence Williams Blue Five. It was in New York that Claude Hopkins invited him to go to Paris with the *Revue Nègre*. Josephine and Bechet met for the first time on the boat that brought them to France.

Baby Darlin

Not all those who appeared in the original *Revue Nègre* came from New York. Beside Louis Douglas, who had been recruited in Paris, there was also a young French West Indian, from Martinique, who was hired for the duration of the Paris run. Fifty years after the event, Madame Mathilde Légitimus remembers how, as a fourteen-year-old named Baby Darlin, she joined the motley crowd of dancers on the stage of the Champs-Élysées Theatre.

Before the arrival of Dudley's troupe in Paris, Mathilde was posing for painters, including Colin, at the Grande Chaumière artists' studios in Montparnasse. Friends took her to one of the first performances of the *Revue Nègre* and then challenged her to dance like the girls on the stage. She promptly went to see Louis Douglas and asked him for a job.

'Can you dance the Charleston, the Black Bottom and do the Cakewalk?' he asked her.

'Yes, all of them,' she lied, without a notion of any of them.

When Douglas auditioned her the next morning he could see at once she was untrained, but he hired her anyway, because, as he said afterwards, she had the *culot* or nerve and self-assurance to ask him, and he liked her for that.

As a young newcomer she found Josephine friendly towards her, perhaps because her own relations with the others was not so good since she had replaced the lead singer, Maud de Forest. Baby Darlin was soon able to repay Josephine's friendliness. A violent incident arose between the star and a musician friend of one of the dancers, whom Josephine had allegedly punched in an argument. The musician swore he'd kill Josephine and set off for her dressing room carrying a knife. Baby Darlin got there first and barricaded the room as the knife-wielding musician hurled insults at Josephine and lunged at the door. The dancer, Joe Alex, was called and a more serious incident was averted.

After her unexpected debut in the *Revue Nègre*, Baby Darlin could not travel with the company when it left Paris, because she was too young to obtain a visa. She continued to work in the theatre, taught dancing for many years, married and founded a dynasty of performers named Légitimus who became in great demand in the cinema and television. Her grandson, Pascal Légitimus, recounted her long career in a television film for the Franco-German ARTE Service. As Darling Légitimus, she was awarded the prize for female roles at the 1983 Venice Film Festival for her performance in *Rue Cases Nègres*.

At our meeting in a Belleville restaurant in eastern Paris, Madame Mathilde Légitimus talked about the past. She had good reason to remember her brief stint in the *Revue Nègre*. It was Josephine who suggested adding the letter 'g' to her original family name, transforming 'Darlin' into the more memorable 'Baby Darling'!

Did she keep contact with Josephine over the years? I asked the woman who no longer danced, but taught others.

'No,' she replied sadly. 'Josephine didn't like her own race very much. There are certain periods of our life I prefer to remain silent about.'

André Daven Remembers

More than thirty years after the event, André Daven, de Maré's associate, was to throw new light on how at least part of the *Revue Nègre* troupe was recruited in New York. Daven's account, published in a French literary weekly, is at variance with what Claude Hopkins remembers and contradicts Jacques-Charles's assertion that he had engaged the American troupe 'unseen'. It also suggests that Caroline Dudley's role was less that of an impresario than of financial 'angel' and escort to the young black dancers, and someone whose main task ended when they stepped off the train in Paris.

Writing in the French literary weekly, *Les Nouvelles Littéraires*, in May 1959, on the occasion of Josephine's appearance at the Olympia music hall in Paris, Daven recalls how, when receipts were falling at the Théâtre des Champs-Élysées, the cubist painter, Fernand Léger, whose scenic designs had contributed to earlier successes at the theatre, recommended to de Maré and Daven that they find a 'gimmick' to attract more people to the theatre. Léger suggested that Daven should go to New York in order to see a fellow artist named Covarrubias, who lived in Harlem. This Mexican painter would show him what Negro performers could do. 'Negroes are dynamite,' Léger assured them. 'Only they can raise the dead!'

Daven asserts that it was in a small New York club in Harlem called The Colonial that he and Miguel Covarrubias auditioned a group of coloured singers, musicians and dancers, who were eventually to form the nucleus of the *Revue Nègre* company.

Miguel Covarrubias, the Mexican artist who contributed scenic designs for the *Revue*, is said by some to have 'selected' Josephine for prominence during rehearsals. And the French

Cubist painter, Fernand Léger, who had designed for de Maré's Swedish Ballet and had suggested that de Maré engage black performers from America, claims to have seen in Josephine the makings of a star performer.

It should also be noted that in their book, Josephine, *Une Vie Mise à Nue*, Jean-Claude Baker and Chris Chase affirm that it was the initial studies of black dancers by Miguel Covarrubias that led to Paul Colin's discovery of Negro images...

The artistes that Covarrubias assembled for Daven's approval convinced him of the viability of a Negro show for Paris. 'It was the purest and most authentic coloured show one could see,' wrote Daven. 'That was how the *Revue Nègre* was born in Harlem – with enthusiasm!'

Josephine was apparently not part of this particular audition and Daven makes no mention of Caroline Dudley in his reminiscences.

The author Elizabeth Kendall brings forward the name of the painter Léger in her book *Where She Danced* (whose title does not specifically refer to Josephine Baker) and writes,

> Bringing Harlem to Paris was the idea of Fernand Léger, the Cubist painter and designer of ballets; he thought of it after writing a scenario for a *ballet Nègre* and then realising it already existed in New York. After Léger had conjured her up [sic] the real Josephine became a further catalyst to the picture-making process at the time, especially the Cubist-influenced theatrical posters, which showed her tall stick-like figure jutting out at knees, elbows and derrière (covered by a little skirt of bananas).

Kendall confirms for good measure the atmosphere prevailing in Paris at the time.

> In Paris and London in the high Twenties, an audience could find itself one night watching the ultra-sophisticated works of the Russian Ballet, and the next the ultra-primitive Charleston of Josephine or the dislocated rhythmic antics of Fred and Adele [Astaire]. Somehow, it was all part of the same world. Styles, degrees of humour, and consciousness or unconsciousness were mixed and juggled and absorbed easily, one into the other.

The co-directors of the Champs-Élysées Theatre remain shadowy figures in the history of the *Revue Nègre*. Rolf de Maré had taken lease of the theatre for five years to present opera and ballet, and had won a certain renown for his Swedish Ballet. When he and his French collaborator, André Daven, decided upon a season of music hall, it was de Maré's last theatrical venture before retiring from the Paris scene. It fell to Daven to engage the artistes available to sustain a complete change of programme every fortnight.

In his biography of Sydney Bechet, Raymond Mouly writes that Daven 'had crossed the Atlantic especially to recruit a Negro troupe that would give Parisians a surprise'. Jacques-Charles, however, asserts that Daven had engaged the troupe 'unseen and on the sole recommendation of an impresario'. He does not name the promoter.

In the face of the explosion of music and dance that Daven and de Maré had unwittingly unleashed during rehearsals at the Champs-Élysées Theatre, de Maré's only recorded comments were, 'Catastrophic!' and to Caroline Dudley in apparent dismay, 'Your calm astonishes me!' De Maré and Daven were no less astonished when their theatre was besieged by *le tout Paris*, including the most prominent literary and intellectual personalities of the day, led by Jean Cocteau, all clamouring to see Josephine. The enormous and unexpected success of the *Revue Nègre* vindicated their policy of presenting music hall entertainment in the Champs-Élysées Theatre and silenced critics who considered they had betrayed the ideals of the founder, Gabriel Astruc, whose temple was dedicated to opera and classical dance.

Concluding Thoughts

In summing up the claims of those most closely involved with the *Revue Nègre*, a pattern of antipathies and 'forgetfulness' emerges concerning the role of others. Thus, Caroline Dudley didn't like Paul Colin and was annoyed by André Daven. Colin reciprocated by calling Dudley a 'zero' and he didn't think much better of his employer, Rolf de Maré. De Maré was apparently out of sympathy with Dudley's methods, while Jacques-Charles reproaches them all for not acknowledging his 'salvage' operation and for forgetting him completely once the *Revue* was put on its feet.

The explosion of energy and sound generated by the troupe on opening night may have had an edge of desperation in it, when one remembers Jacques-Charles's threat to send the company home. But the acclamation that greeted Josephine Baker was of a kind reserved only for exceptional performers. Overnight, all Paris was talking about was Josephine in the *Revue Nègre*. Daven and de Maré promptly forgot their earlier anxiety, extended the run of the review beyond the originally advertised fortnight, and sat back with relief to make the most of their unexpected popular success. The one person to suffer from the whole business was Maud de Forest, the blues singer, whom no one seemed to miss once she had been pushed into the background, but who continued to sing after the *Revue* was disbanded. Alas for Maud, her name was not even spelled correctly on the playbills, and her greatest claim to fame is that she once recorded with the Fletcher Henderson band.

More than half a century after the event, at the age of eighty-eight, Paul Colin takes a somewhat cynical view of the *Revue Nègre* and Josephine's sudden emergence.

'People tell stories without knowing anything about it,' he said reproachfully, sitting in his rooftop studio near the Champs-Élysées. While admitting he owed much to the success of his poster and his association with the *Revue Nègre*, Colin also avers it was no more than a revue among many others for which he had designed equally successful posters.

Colin took a poor view of de Maré whom he described as a 'Swede with a big fortune' who had taken the lease of the theatre in order to present Jean Borlin. 'When one had seen Borlin for fifteen days, it was enough!'

Fully occupied with his job as scene painter and poster designer, Colin was apparently unaware of Jacques-Charles's intervention during rehearsals. And as for Caroline Dudley's role in Paris, he was brief and to the point.

'Zero! Never saw her! We had nothing to do with her. She advised de Maré to take the *Revue*. She didn't do more than that.

She came to see me several times to protest...' About what, he remains silent.

Colin readily acknowledges that Josephine had a superb body '...but she danced the Charleston no better than many other Negresses of that time... all of them good and many of them better-looking... Negroes are much more supple, more human than the French...'

Paul Colin's 'Art Deco'-style poster had captured the spirit of the *Revue Nègre* and greatly helped to popularise Josephine and the *Revue*. His poster became a highly prized collectors' item and their two names were henceforth linked professionally, but they were never to meet again.

As for Josephine's later career, Paul Colin asserts that it was the journalists who made her. 'The press seized on her because she had arrived from America and brought a new style.' However, he concedes that Josephine had a greater intelligence than many and knew how to use it to promote herself and keep her name before the public. 'I wasn't struck by her character, but she was intelligent,' Colin repeated several times. Whatever he thought of black dance from Harlem, Paul Colin was impressed enough by the success of the *Revue Nègre* to promote his own Negro Ball in the Champs-Élysées Theatre in 1927. His poster for the *Bal Nègre* echoed the animated style of his design for the *Revue Nègre*, and reputedly attracted three thousand people in one evening; but he would not admit that the dancer he had depicted was modelled on Josephine, or that his work had been influenced by the artist Covarrubias.

Others have claimed to have recognised Josephine's talents and potential even before she made her breakthrough in Paris. Noble Sissle, a black producer, had auditioned Josephine in New York in 1921, when she was fifteen, and testifies to 'her magnetic personality emanating from the chorus line'. Sissle's partner, Eubie Blake, said he taught her the elements of her profession when she was sixteen and joined their road-show company.

Caroline Dudley and Josephine Baker

This leaves only the two women most intimately concerned with the phenomenon of the *Revue Nègre*, Caroline Dudley, who conceived the idea of presenting black American music and dance in Paris, and Josephine Baker, who became its chief beneficiary.

Living a secluded life in the South of France, Caroline Dudley, the widow of the French novelist Joseph Delteil, recalls the time when, as a young woman in New York half a century ago, she first had what she calls the 'crazy idea' of putting on a show in Paris. Madame Delteil freely admits she took on more than she could comfortably handle when she brought twenty-five unknown artistes across the Atlantic to face critical Parisian audiences.

'Without the work done by my sisters, Catherine and Dorothy, I would have died!' she exclaimed. 'Oh, my God, I had such responsibility, and I was always terrified that they wouldn't appear.' But Madame Delteil made no mention of Jacques-Charles…

As the wife of Joseph Delteil, Caroline Dudley put behind her the short-lived but memorable foray into French music hall entertainment and immersed herself into her husband's literary life. She followed Josephine's career at a distance and admired how she had cultivated her voice. The last time they met was on the steps of the Palais de Justice in Paris in 1926, when Dudley renounced the legal action she had brought against Josephine for breach of contract. As Dudley remarked, concerning the incident years later, 'Financial investment? It cost me quite a bit. I put money into the *Revue Nègre* and – au revoir!'

Joseph Delteil later viewed his wife's experience in an historical context when he wrote, 'Josephine's eccentricity appealed to surrealists such as André Breton and Soupault, who had broken away from the destructive Dadaists to become constructively non-conformist. A creature described as "not man, not woman", who responded with such archaic fervour to the most logical of music, appealed to their own sense of improbability and ambiguity.'

Josephine for her part had apparently remained ignorant of the initial crisis over the viability of the *Revue Nègre*. She was also, for many years, unaware of the identity of the person who claimed to have put the revue on its feet and who had chosen her for a more prominent role.

In her posthumous autobiography, compiled in collaboration with her second French husband, Josephine favours Paul Colin, who had befriended her on her arrival in Paris. It was under Colin's gaze that she discovered the beauty of her own body when he drew her, and it was Colin who took her to the celebrated 'couturier' Paul Poiret, to be fitted for her first real Parisian evening gown. But Colin's intervention with the *Revue* management goes unmentioned in her book.

Neither is there mention of her meeting with Jacques-Charles years later when she reportedly thanked him with tears in her eyes for having launched her career. Her legal tussle with Caroline Dudley is dismissed with the artless remark, 'Madame Dudley didn't want to let me go. It wasn't my fault!'

It will never be known for certain who first saw in Josephine the future star she was to become. The truth probably is that, sooner or later, given the opportunity, she would eventually have established herself, as she had already done in New York. When the opportunity again presented itself in Paris she seized it and created a new role for herself in the *Revue Nègre*.

Two other factors helped to give Josephine Baker's arrival and 'discovery' in Paris the character of an event. Unlike those who had been seen to struggle in their theatrical careers, Josephine's earlier apprenticeship in the chorus line was unknown outside America. The fact that she had never before appeared in Europe gave her the added advantage of surprise when she burst on to the Paris scene. Audiences immediately responded to her natural grace and boundless energy, and the process was supplemented by the press, which almost unanimously proclaimed the arrival of the 'Black Venus'!

The theatrical form of the *Revue Nègre* aided Josephine's consecration as an exotic being. It was not a revue in the strict sense of the term (literally a re-viewing of the personalities and events of the past year), but a hastily assembled series of tableaux peopled by artistes of varying talents whose only common feature was that they were all of Negro origin and expressed themselves in the Afro-American musical idiom. The absence of a musical structure or theme allowed Josephine to easily outshine her fellow artistes and dominate the show.

Top: First poster to announce the *Revue Nègre* gave little hint of what was in store for Parisians in 1925.
Bottom: The hastily conceived programme began to depict members of the troupe.

LES MÉMOIRES DE
JOSÉPHINE BAKER

The French poet and journalist, Marcel Sauvage, wrote the first biography of Josephine Baker in 1927, when Josephine was only nineteen years old.

For her debut at the Folies Bergère, Josephine adopted necklets and bracelets and slicked-down hair.
Collection Cinémathèque Francaise.

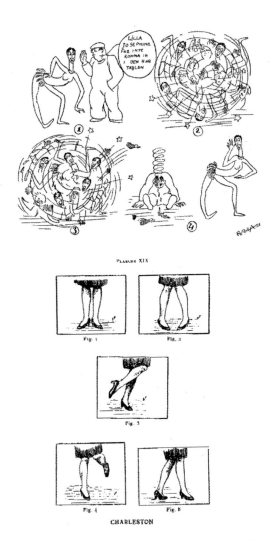

Top: Josephine's energetic demonstration of the Charleston was frequently caricatured in the European Press.
Bottom: The Charleston.

Top: Paul Colin, the designer, shared Josephine's celebrity after he created his poster for the *Revue Nègre*.
Bottom: Living in seclusion in the south of France in 1980, Caroline Dudley-Delteil with her daughter and the author, recalls bringing Josephine to Paris from New York in 1925.

Top: Josephine clowns in a Paris restaurant seated between Pepito Abatino on her left and the Belgian writer, Georges Simenon. *Bottom:* The celebrated Belgian novelist, Georges Simenon, became one of Josephine's ardent admirers from 1926.

The girdle of rhinestone-studded artificial bananas, created by the Paris fashion designer Paul Poiret for Josephine's debut at the Folies Bergère in 1927, became her trademark and symbol.

Josephine arrives at Croydon airport for her London debut at the Prince Edward Theatre, in October 1933.

Chapter Three
'Who was Josephine Baker?'
New York in the Twenties

Who was Josephine Baker? Where did she come from? From the moment she leapt into public view in Europe these questions were asked, and some of the most improbable answers were offered.

The Spanish newspaper, *Noche*, published in Barcelona, once suggested that Josephine's real family name was Vaquer, or Baquer, common in Catalonia and Americanised by the introduction of a 'K' to produce Baker ! It was a vain attempt to link her and her natural father (who was said to be of Spanish origin) to an Iberian homeland. The truth was to be found elsewhere. The name by which Josephine was almost universally known was but one of several family names to which she was legally entitled, and came from an early second marriage in 1921 to a black American, William Howard Baker, in Philadelphia, when she was fifteen.

Josephine's early life in America became a source of legends in which no amount of exaggeration and fantasy seemed too far-fetched for the public image she presented. That Josephine was *métisse*, was clearly seen from her skin colour and physiognomy. The sobriquets 'Black Venus' and 'Bird of Paradise' merely added to the mystery and fed the imagination. When she first appeared on the world stage she possessed an instant appeal that surpassed colour or physique.

Josephine first treated questions about her origin lightly and was amused to be the object of so much curiosity. The answers she gave to impatient journalists more often clouded the truth than clarified points of fact. She had her own reasons for not revealing details of her early life. She lived in the present and could barely bring herself to think about the future, let alone recall the past. She consequently resorted to inventing a family history.

An example of Josephine's powers of imagination is related by Michel Georges-Michel in *Nuits d'Actrices* (1933).

As Josephine told it, her father was an itinerant salesman of Indian textiles. A white pastor would go ahead of him into Texan villages and tell the black women there that white men were offended by their bare shoulders and that they would never be accepted in polite society. The next day Josephine's father would arrive in his little car, blowing a trumpet to announce his sale of cloth. To the women, the trumpet call sounded like the Last Judgement, and they fell on their knees in the village square. Her father then unrolled bales of cloth and dazzled them with its colours. When he had sold all he could he moved on and joined his colleague, the pastor, in the mountains where they shared out the spoils. And then they were off again to the next village, the pastor preaching the evils of bare shoulders...

What happened then? Josephine's listeners probably asked. She brought the story to a conclusion by telling that the white pastor was not content with his share of the money. 'My father could not hit back,' said Josephine, 'because his white colleague threatened to have him strung up [lynched]. And so their association came to an end.'

It was a curious tale with echoes of white injustice towards blacks, in an audacious 'hard sell' operation that Barnum himself would have been proud of. Georges-Michel adds in his account that each time he heard Josephine tell such stories they would vary in detail.

The moment Josephine left New York and crossed the Atlantic for the first time she put behind her a life she (temporarily) wanted to forget, and which she felt free to reinvent when the occasion demanded.

One of the first people to seek out Josephine for a personal account of her origins was a reporter on *l'Intransigeant*, the Paris newspaper. The journalist and poet, Marcel Sauvage, was on board an Italian cargo boat off Nice in October 1925 when he first heard from a crewman of Josephine Baker's theatrical success in

Paris. On reading an account in Marseilles of her appearance in the *Revue Nègre* Sauvage resolved to find out more about the dancer everyone was talking about.

The result was the first biography of Josephine, entitled *Les Mémoires de Joséphine Baker*, published in 1927. In it one reads in print for the first time Josephine declaring, 'I was born in Bernard Street, St. Louis, on 3 June 1906.'

There has always been a slight doubt about Josephine's generally accepted birth date. One of her former agents, Stephen Papich, who travelled with her on tours, claims in his book of souvenirs, *Remembering Josephine*, to have seen in her passport the birth date 1903, later to be amended to 1906. As late as 1949, the United States Press Association wire service gave her birth date as 1903. In 1963 the *Celebrity Register* published by Harper and Row gives Josephine's year of birth as 1907!

At a press conference given by Josephine at the Hilton Hotel in New York in 1963, a journalist addressed her, saying he didn't wish to be impolite but he wanted to know how old she was. Josephine replied at once, 'You are not impolite at all. I'm sixty!' Was it a ship of tongue, or simply a convenient round figure (when she would have been only fifty-seven) that came into her head and brought us back to 1903?

In a second biography by André Rivolet, published in 1935, entitled *Une Vie de Toutes les Couleurs*, Josephine herself recounts that the passport issued to her in New York to leave for Europe in 1925 bore the date 3 June 1906, based on her birth certificate obtained from City Hall, St. Louis. But she admits that in order to obtain her passport she told the authorities she was older. In fact, she was already legally an adult and had no need of making a false declaration.

In his pictorial record of a later period of Josephine's life in France, Jean-Claude Bonnal[*] writes that searches carried out at the National Records Office in the US and in the State of Missouri failed to produce Josephine's birth certificate. A correspondent from a research and development institute says

---

[*] *Josephine Baker et le village des enfants du monde en Périgord*, Collection Centaurée Fleur de Lys, 1992.

that before computerisation old records were kept by municipalities, whether of cities, townships, counties of state, and that many earlier handwritten records have been lost.

Perhaps the most telling evidence that Josephine might have been born earlier than 1906 is to be seen on her Certificate and Record of Marriage, held in the Bureau of Vital Statistics in the State of New Jersey. On it one reads that on 17 September 1921 Josephine married William H Baker, a coloured man aged twenty-three, in Philadelphia. Josephine's age on the attested certificate is given as nineteen, which takes us back to... 1902 as the birth date! There, on that document we have at least the origin of the name Baker, derived from her second marriage. Yet for all the possible discrepancies over the year of her birth, the lettering on her black granite tomb in Monaco reaffirms her lifespan as 1906–1975.

Put simply, most accounts state that Josephine was born on 3 June 1906, in St. Louis, Missouri, of a black American mother and a European father. According to her younger sister Margarette, it was eleven o'clock on a Sunday morning, 3 June, that their mother Carrie McDonald, aged twenty-one, gave birth in the maternity hospital to her first child, a five-pound baby girl named Freda. As Carrie was not married she sent baby Josephine to live with her grandmother, who in turn lived with her sister, Carrie's aunt Elvara; they were Cherokee Indians. Little Freda was subsequently named Josephine after Carrie's cousin.

The shame perceived by Josephine of having been born out of wedlock caused her to avoid mention of her natural father, the man who loved and left Carrie, never to reappear. When detailing her family – 'a great-grandmother, a grandmother, my mother, my brother, my two sisters' – Josephine often added evasively, 'My father wasn't there. He worked far away.'

Josephine later said, 'My father and my mother met at school. My father was Spanish. His family didn't want them to marry. They were very poor and abandoned. My father went away to find work and never returned.'

Josephine's father is variously described as 'a Jewish travelling salesman', 'a drummer', 'a European adventurer who disregarded the dangers of the black ghetto of St. Louis to possess the beautiful black Carrie'. His name varies from 'Isaac Ravelle' to

'Eddie Moreno' or 'Carson'. From some accounts Eddie was a good-looking Spaniard with olive skin who courted Carrie at neighbourhood dances every Sunday. Josephine later affirmed that Eddie finally seduced Carrie in a cinema after meeting her out of school. But he never married her. Josephine's sister Margarette affirmed to the writer that Eddie was Spanish.

Carrie McDonald did not stay unmarried for long, a descendant of Negro slaves, she was tall and good-looking. Their ancestors, black African and American Indian, had migrated from the south in search of work. Carrie and her mother had arrived in St. Louis in 1904, to live with sister Elvara, who had lost her husband in the Spanish-American war and lived on a small pension. When Arthur Martin, the son of an African slave, appeared on the scene he agreed to marry Carrie and bring up Josephine. They moved into a one-room shack in the black ghetto of Boxcar Town.

As doyenne of the clan, Josephine's Aunt Elvara stoutly defended her Indian ancestry. Josephine remembers her as a huge woman with copper-coloured skin and coral black hair in two long braids, sitting smoking a pipe. After a glass of whisky she would sometimes rise and perform a few tribal dance steps. But she was just as likely to explode with anger against what she called the 'new American'. She tore into her sister for having taken a white lover instead of what she called a 'real American' – that is, an Indian. True to her character, she reproached Carrie for marrying a black instead of an Indian. For Aunt Elvara it was Indian blood that counted the most.

If her birth date is to be accepted, Josephine was born a few weeks after the great earthquake and fire that destroyed San Francisco in 1906. That catastrophe, which rocked the State of California three thousand miles away, could have happened on another planet for all the impact made on the black quarter of St. Louis. Even the World's Fair, held in the previous year in the city, hardly touched the lives of those who lived in poverty and squalor in Boxcar Town. Most were even below the reach of the severe economic depression that hit the United States from 1907.

Josephine grew up with the emergence of modern American society, but Americans of African origin were then far from enjoying equal rights as US citizens. When slavery was abolished in 1865 the American Negro became a freedman but not a free man. Segregation and discrimination remained rife despite the decrees of the 14th and 15th Amendments to the Constitution, which removed race and colour as obstacles to full citizenship.

In the first decade of the century there were ten million Negroes in the United States, making up almost 11 per cent of the entire population. Most lived in eleven states that had made up the Southern Confederacy. A small proportion lived in four states bordering the former Confederacy: Delaware, Maryland, Kentucky and Missouri. There were some five thousand Negroes living on the south side of St. Louis, a fur-trading post set up by the French on the Mississippi River which later became a major industrialised city. The writer Mark Twain refers to it as having the nation's most polluted air. And to those in the black ghetto, it seemed perpetually cold.

Arthur Martin's family was no poorer than most black families in Boxcar Town. Their home was one room with one bed and a cooking stove made from an oil drum. Josephine soon had a younger brother and two younger sisters to help her mother look after. Carrie sent Josephine out on errands and to scrub floors for a few cents. When her younger brother, Richard, and her younger sisters, Margarette and Willie Mae, were old enough, Josephine led them on expeditions to the railway tracks to collect lumps of coal from the parked wagons. They gathered discarded rotten vegetables from under market stalls and returned home to make soup from chicken heads found in waste bins.

Josephine was always the most adventurous and extrovert member of the family. When not performing chores she danced to music on improvised instruments such as cooking pots, wooden cases and an old comb and tissue paper. When she was sent to school she continually made faces and her teachers said she would come to a bad end. She was always clowning to gain attention and her legs itched to move and dance. In church on Sundays it was Josephine who sang the loudest, and put all her faith in God. Edouard Beaudu later wrote,

As a child in the State of Missouri, not even the poverty in which

she grew up could suppress her mischievousness nor an
irresistible desire to amuse those around her. She couldn't care
less that she was called a monkey. For she was, in reality, singled
out by destiny to teach us the Charleston!

Riot and Massacre

When Josephine was eight her mother sent her out to live and
work as a servant in a white household. She was willing and
energetic but she found the tasks she was given demeaning and
she was frequently beaten and ill-treated. When she changed her
employer a new threat arose. The husband of the household
began to make sexual advances to her at night. When she tearfully
told the mistress of the house she was immediately sent home.

Josephine was growing up at a time when America was on the
move. Motor cars, mass-circulation magazines and industries
were changing the face of the land. The coloured advertisements
Arthur Martin had pasted on the walls to brighten their home
showed smiling, well-dressed couples in spacious homes or out of
doors, enjoying activities Josephine had never seen, like adult
sports and family outings… But it was also a world peopled
exclusively by whites.

As her limited horizons widened Josephine began to perceive
that there were two worlds beyond Boxcar Town: a world of
black and coloured people of which she was a part; and a world
inhabited by people with material wealth and influence who made
the rules. On the one hand there was poverty, hardship and
oppression, and on the other, power, influence and happiness.

Nothing Josephine had seen or heard brought these
differences into greater focus than the bloody riot and massacre
that swept through east St. Louis when she was eleven. On 2 July
1917, Josephine was awoken urgently by Carrie who hurried the
family out of the door into the street under a sky red with flames
and black smoke. Bands of whites intent on arson and murder
descended on the black ghetto, setting fire to shacks and attacking
the inhabitants fleeing across the Mississippi Eads Bridge.

The incident left fifty dead and some six thousand homeless.
Rioters reportedly burned a black theatre and some of the women
and children attending the performance died in the flames or

were shot to death running from the fire. White women and boys were part of the mobs. Damage was estimated at more than half a million dollars. The threat of insecurity and danger made an indelible impression on Josephine.

The reason for the revolt was attributed to whites' fear of unemployment due to the massive incursion of black immigrants from the rural South to the northern industrial centres. A Congressional investigation officially placed responsibility for the dead and injured on 'industrial and railroad interests'. It was also a time when coloured men were being enlisted in the regular army to fight in the war in Europe 'to defend democracy'. While the White House in Washington remained silent over the repeated oppression of blacks, the dreaded secret white supremacist organisation, the Ku Klux Klan, had grown to number five million members.

After the riot the family moved to new shared lodgings which included a cellar in which Josephine and her sisters played. They created a makeshift stage in which Josephine gave improvised 'performances' for the neighbourhood children. The entrance fee was one pin. 'If you don't sit down and watch, I'll punch you...' was Josephine's way of gaining the attention of her audience. Wrapped in an old curtain, she would then gesture and sweep about in a manner she imagined real actresses did. Once there was near disaster when her trailing curtain was caught alight from the candles that served to light the cellar. Everyone rushed screaming from the house and the game was abandoned.

Josephine had only once visited a real theatre. It was in Philadelphia with her grandmother when she was ten. She sensed that in make-believe there was an escape from the oppressive real world that surrounded her. She dreamed of passing through that invisible barrier to the other side where she could pretend to be someone else, somewhere else.

First Marriage

Almost by chance Josephine's life took an unexpected turn. After a family quarrel one evening Josephine slammed the door and found herself tearfully wandering down the street, alone. A local tradesman who knew her by sight saw his chance and invited her in. When Josephine began openly to live with him it became a neighbourhood scandal; the man was in his fifties and Josephine was barely thirteen. When the pressure of local opinion became too great, Josephine went to live with grandmother McDonald, and took a job as a waitress to bring in some money. She quickly made the acquaintance of a foundry worker in his late twenties named Willie Arthur Wells.

Within months they were married in a ceremony performed by a pastor at the home of a relative. Josephine left her job and began to live in their one-room home preparing baby clothes and a cot.

The marriage was short-lived. After a violent and bloody fight one evening, Willie Wells stormed out, never to return to his wife. Josephine went back to her job. No child ever made its appearance. The episode was never referred to in later years. Even the name of her first legal husband vanished with a later marriage. Josephine was left only with a greater desire to escape from the confines of Boxcar Town.

It was a trio of local musicians known as the Jones Family Band who brought Josephine into the orbit of the theatre. Realising her desire to sing and dance they asked her to join them in busking around the town. Soon they were invited to do a turn at the local Booker T Washington theatre. As the youngest member of the group, Josephine improvised wild dances to the music they played and was rewarded with ecstatic applause. She had made contact with an audience and would ever after seek to renew the experience. When a professional troupe called the Dixie Steppers came to town Josephine resolved to join them.

Josephine Joins the Dixie Steppers

One day Josephine sought out the manager of the Dixie Steppers, Bob Russell, and asked him for a job. At a brief audition he saw at once that she was completely untrained as a dancer. But she made such an extraordinary spectacle of herself trying to emulate the others that he decided to take her on – as a Cupid with wings suspended on a wire above the heads of the actors.

Josephine's first professional appearance was a disaster. Floating into sight, holding the traditional bow and arrow above a couple of stage lovers, she became hopelessly entangled in the scenery, and stopped the show. The audience went wild with laughter as she struggled to free herself. The scene became a fiasco. Josephine was sure that it was the end of her engagement. In fact it was the beginning of her professional stage career.

Russell saw at once that the unrehearsed incident drew more laughter and applause than all the other acts put together. He hired her to perform the same contrived interruption each night they played that scene. If she wanted to come on tour she could help out as dresser for the remainder of the time on the road. That was all Josephine wanted to hear...

As a gesture of independence Josephine cut her hair short and announced that she was leaving home to go on the road, not as a performer but as a dresser, stagehand, and general dogsbody – and the occasional Cupid when that role was called for. To the end of her days her sister Margarette could not understand how Josephine had managed to persuade the manager of the Dixie Steppers to take her on. But she knew better than anyone else how desperately Josephine needed to strike out for herself.

Race and Colour in the Twenties

It was while on tour in the American vaudeville theatre that Josephine first became aware of the difficulties the colour of her skin could present. Even before she had left home she had experienced the fury of race riots. Later as she travelled America she became aware of the limited place granted to coloured people in the life of the country.

Born of a Negro mother with part-Indian blood and a Spanish father, Josephine was a mulatto whose 'café au lait' complexion revealed her mixed racial origins. Among whites she was considered 'chocolate coloured', while blacks called her a 'pinkie'.

The Afro-American poet, Langston Hughes, once remarked, 'Negro blood is sure powerful – because just *one* drop of black blood makes a coloured man. *One* drop and you're a Negro! Black is powerful!'

But to Americans in the Twenties, the colour black was considered neither powerful nor beautiful. Not only did it create fear and loathing among the white population, but variations also produced doubts and discrimination among racially pure Negroes of African origin, and jealousy among indigenous American Indians.

By its nature a road tour company was a self-contained unit whose main concern was to pay its way until the next town was reached. The Theatre Owners' Booking Association, whose initials TOBA were ironically said to mean 'Tough on Black Actors', attempted to route troupes on a never-ending circuit of play dates. Lodgings were often makeshift dormitories with minimum comfort, frequently paid for with free tickets to the show to help fill empty seats. In the Southern States many respectable Negroes would not let showgirls into their homes. When they went to the show they in turn sometimes found a rope stretched down the middle of the hall to keep white and coloured customers apart.

On the Road

When Josephine left home in St. Louis she embarked on a life that would be full of pitfalls and detours. The Dixie Steppers tour took her through the Southern and Western States. The camaraderie of the troupe gave her a sense of security, and thanks to her age she was considered the baby of the company. When she had little else to do she studied an 'alphabet book', given to her by one of the troupe, to help her read and write. The manager called her 'String bean' because of her thin build and growing height. But he also remarked, 'One thing will never change – her colour. In my line of girls she makes a white gap!'

When Josephine had replaced a truly dark-skinned dancer who had fallen and injured herself, she was obliged to 'black up' to make her complexion blend with the other performers. It was the first time she had danced in the chorus line. She passed the test, but as a clown. Her exaggerated antics drew attention to her, and the grimaces and eye-rolling that had provoked reprimands at school enabled her to stay on the payroll when her flying Cupid act was abandoned. She was put at the end of the chorus line as the comic 'end-girl', and paid ten dollars a week.

When the troupe arrived to play in New Orleans, Mr Russell suddenly announced that he could no longer keep Josephine in the company. Too much of an individualist, the more effort she put into her dancing, the more she stood out. 'What was a string bean doing in a can of identical peas...?' he asked himself. Coloured artistes were plentiful and the management had no need of her individualism. She had danced herself out of a job.

Heartbroken at being abandoned, Josephine allowed the latent obstinacy in her character to assert itself. She promptly stowed away in a costume basket and re-emerged at the next stop after a long train journey, pleading to be kept on. Her dramatic gesture paid off – for a short time.

In Philadelphia it was the end of the Dixie Steppers; Mr Russell announced the company was disbanding; it was everyone for himself. Feeling like a trooper after her first professional tour, Josephine accepted the inevitable.

Josephine's disappointment and loneliness drove her into the arms of a man who had recently befriended her at a party. Willie Howard Baker was a railway Pullman porter in his twenties and, like Josephine, he enjoyed travel and adventure. In September they eloped to Camden, New Jersey, and were married by a Justice of the Peace. Regulations were less strict than in Pennsylvania; the marriage certificate shows Josephine to be nineteen when she would have been only a few months more than fifteen.

Josephine took her new husband back to St. Louis to meet her family, possibly to prove that if she could not stay in a roadshow she could at least get another husband. When the couple returned to Philadelphia, the attraction of New York, only two hours away, began to assert itself.

Among her friends there was talk of a new show being tried out in Philadelphia before going on Broadway in New York. Josephine sought out members of the new cast who remembered seeing her at the Gibson Theatre with the Dixie Steppers. They agreed to take her to see the producers of the new show at the Dunbar Theatre.

Noble Sissle and Eubie Blake were an up-and-coming songwriting team who were already the talk of New York. Blake, the son of an ex-slave, played the piano; Sissle, a minister's son, wrote lyrics. Together with two comedians, Flouroy Miller and

Aubrey Lyles, they were creating a Negro show that would be more like a white musical comedy than coloured vaudeville. In a radical break from the usual practice of featuring blacked-up artistes for white audiences, Sissle and Blake were recruiting light-skinned chorus girls. The show was to be called *Shuffle Along*.

Noble Sissle tells of his first encounter with Josephine – 'a slender, nervous little girl whose big brown eyes shone like saucers as the raindrops clustered on her tender olive skin.

'Just as we were about to say, yes, you may join our show, Miller called me aside and said, "Sissle, that kid looks awfully young to me." When we asked her how old she was she immediately replied, "I'm fifteen." Well, the law of New York did not permit the use of chorus girls under the age of sixteen. We stood there, the four of us, as she slowly walked down the steps leading down to the stage door exit. Then without even looking back she disappeared into the rain.'

Noble Sissle concludes his anecdote by admitting that 'it was one of the most poignant experiences of my life, an unforgettable first meeting with someone who was destined to become a great international star.'

New York in the Twenties

New York in the 1920s was the capital of the American entertainment industry. Radio was in its infancy, television non-existent, and motion pictures were still silent black and white novelties. Live theatre, vaudeville and cabaret reigned supreme.

There were sixty-three theatres on Broadway, and in one season alone, thirty music shows ran simultaneously. Harlem was the Negro centre of the city where the Cotton Club dominated entertainment, catering to both black and white audiences. Sunday night was the big night when an average of five hundred well-heeled guests paid to admire twenty beautiful girls in the floor show. Liquor flowed freely. Prohibition and mob rule imposed its own law. Competitors were ruthlessly eliminated if they did not pay, and play along.

Black artistes who gravitated to New York quickly found that there were too many blacks chasing too few jobs. Skin colour was an added complication. Josephine's 'high yaller' complexion, not white, not black, but an unblemished *café crème*, was no more acceptable on the New York stage than it had been elsewhere. To black audiences she was considered a 'pinkie', while whites saw her as 'chocolate coloured'. Managements preferred things to be clear-cut, black or white. Coloured and light-skinned performers found themselves obliged to 'black up' to make audiences think they were whites with black faces in the manner of Al Jolson. The saving grace for Josephine was that she was a comic in whom any difference from the norm was considered as part of her act.

Colour Confusion

Josephine had chosen one of the few occupations in which a coloured girl in the United States could travel and confront white Americans without suffering indignity or overt abuse. She had already worked as a domestic servant and a waitress; vaudeville offered those with talent and the necessary stamina an escape from a menial role and a degree of dignity. But Josephine's so-called 'high yaller' complexion, neither white nor black, which had begun to give her trouble on the road, still presented problems.

Since the end of the nineteenth century, white comedians with black faces had caricatured 'darky' characters, creating a mythical 'coon' image which had become the mainstay of the minstrel idiom in songs and sketches. In a reversal of roles, coloured performers had begun to imitate white artistes *imitating black performers*! Confusion reigned over the respective true role of white and black artistes, and audiences were sometimes unsure if a comedian was actually white or black. After seeing a Negro company perform without burnt cork make-up in 1913, the *New York Dramatic Mirror* complained, 'The prevailing complexion of coloured players is pink...'

As confusion spread throughout the entertainment profession, some managements even demanded that light-skinned artistes black up to pretend to be white performers with black faces. The result was that coloured artistes actually blacked up to play before Negro audiences!

Sissle and Blake thought to reverse the trend, claiming that coloured artistes were equal to any on their own terms and had no need to try to conceal their racial identity. Their policy of presenting light-skinned chorus girls who danced and sang was a deliberate break with tradition.

Shuffle Along

Shuffle Along opened at the Cort Theatre on 63rd Street in New York City on 21 May 1921 and was an immediate success. Not only was it the first Negro show to play on Broadway in a decade, it was the first ever all-coloured show entirely written, produced and performed by African Americans. Built around a slender story of rivalry between two contenders for the office of a local mayor, played by Miller and Lyles with their cross-talk sketches, the show featured Lotti Gee as the star and a chorus line of sixteen light-skinned girls dancing to a score by Sissle and Blake that included 'I'm Just Wild About Harry', a song destined to become a standard. It also brought the sound of jazz to musical comedy.

Shuffle Along helped to launch a number of future celebrities: Florence Mills began her short-lived career on the chorus line, while a young singer straight out of college stood in briefly as one of the Four Harmony Kings. It was Paul Robeson's stage debut and was to lead to his key role in *Show Boat* in New York and London, and worldwide acclaim.

Back in Philadelphia, after her brief visit to St. Louis with her new husband, Josephine remained convinced that it was her (relatively) dark colour, and not her young age, that had caused her to be turned down for *Shuffle Along*. Now that she was going on sixteen she resolved to have another try at joining the troupe. Leaving husband Willie at home, she took the train for New York.

Shuffle Along had become so successful on Broadway that a touring company was set up to play one-night appearances across the country. When Josephine turned up for the interview, she had taken the precaution of powdering her face and neck to lighten her complexion. She found Sissle and Blake's white partner, Al Mayer, auditioning the second cast. He hired her at once to be end-girl on the chorus line at thirty dollars a week. Persistence had paid off. Josephine was now on the payroll of the touring company of the show making theatrical history in New York.

Home Again

During Josephine's coast-to-coast tour, *Shuffle Along* played in St. Louis and Josephine once again visited her old home, this time without her husband. It was both an exhilarating and a sad homecoming. The fact that it was a few days to Christmas added poignancy to the occasion. Her ostentatious arrival by taxi from the theatre contrasted sharply with the run-down quarter in which her family lived. When Josephine confronted them in her fine clothes, she found her mother, stepfather, brother and sisters all living in a one-room basement in a limbo of squalor and indolence.

Her mother, Carrie, visited the theatre to watch the show and seemed indifferent to her daughter's achievement. After criticising what she perceived to be the shamelessness of the women, she chastised Josephine as though she was still a child. Her grandmother was more philosophical about Josephine's way of life, and her sister renewed her affection for her. For a few brief hours the family was united and Christmas was celebrated with unaccustomed seasonal fare and gifts.

Josephine's fleeting visit home ended with embraces and promises to return next year and to send money to educate her little sister, Willie May. Josephine rejoined the troupe and went back on the road. She began to send regular payments to help the family, but it would be fourteen years before she would again set foot in St. Louis.

Discovery

The touring company was no 'tent show' living from hand to mouth, but a troupe benefiting from all the prestige of a Broadway hit. Advance publicity was assured. Many of the performers were experienced professionals, together with newcomers of acknowledged talent. Josephine was in good company and truly on the road to a future career as Josephine Baker; the husband who had given her his name was left behind in Philadelphia, all but forgotten.

Among the press reports that came back to New York of the touring company's reception in various cities, Sissle and Blake began to read about 'a certain unprogrammed chorus girl on the end of the line whose mugging and ad-lib clowning were stopping the show'. Curious to see this unrehearsed element, Sissle and his colleague went to Brooklyn to see a Wednesday afternoon performance.

'Sure enough,' recalls Noble Sissle, 'it was Josephine, the young lady we had met in Philadelphia six months previously.' Backstage, there was an anxious moment when they met; Josephine was terrified of being sent away. The creators of the show assured her it was all right, she could stay. There was even better news. They told her that when the travelling company closed for the summer, she could come and join the Broadway show in New York. Josephine burst into tears of jubilation and gratitude.

Noble Sissle adds this compliment to the young performer who became their star. 'Many times we watched her from the wings and Josephine would be bubbling over with such a variety of emotionally inspired antics – none of which she remembered when she came offstage – that it was difficult to keep up with them. Her talents seemed to have been God-given because whenever she hit the stage her magnetic personality exploded directly into the audience. On every occasion her dancing would stop the show.'

News of *Shuffle Along* had reached Paris where the already celebrated music hall performer Maurice Chevalier had achieved a triumph in the musical comedy *Dédé*. On his first visit to New York, in the company of Mistinguett and her new partner, Earl Leslie, Chevalier was curious to see the source of black music and dance that had accompanied Mistinguett in her earlier success in *Paris qui Jazze* at the Casino de Paris.

In *Shuffle Along*, Chevalier found, 'a different artistic rhythm from anything I had known until then in Paris or London'. In his memoirs he noted that, 'among the chorus girls I particularly noticed one whose naked body held strange attractions. Her convulsed and contorted face would suddenly give way to moments of delightful, seductive, relaxation'. It didn't take him long to identify Josephine Baker among the names of the black dancers printed in the programme.

Chevalier admits that 'the evening's performance impressed

me to the highest degree and led me to modify my stage behaviour... There was a force, a frenzy, a physical thrust against which all the literature and all the intellectuality of the world were powerless'. Chevalier was so impressed that he even took a three-week course in dancing lessons. Twenty years later, Chevalier and Josephine would find themselves on the same playbill in unusual circumstances.

For the next three years, Josephine worked under the personal guidance of Sissle and Blake. In New York, her appearance as end-girl in the chorus line became a major attraction and she was paid $125 a week for her inspired clowning.

Many people noticed that even among many talented coloured artistes, Josephine stood out and was somehow different. A New York reporter writing of *Shuffle Along* in 1924 gave Josephine an anonymous notice when he referred to 'the girl who plays marbles with her eyes!' It was an unmistakable reference to Josephine and her habit of rolling her eyes.

Josephine was dubbed the 'unknown star' by another journalist who sought her out in the chorus girls' dressing room after the performance. When he asked her to write her name on a piece of paper, he realised that she expressed herself more easily in physical gestures than in handwriting.

Shuffle Along ran for 504 performances and spawned no fewer than twenty coloured shows on Broadway. One of them, *Chocolate Dandies*, at the Colonial Theatre in September 1924, had Josephine appearing with Bob Williams and a new eccentric dancer and clown named Johnny Hudgins.

Josephine Sets Sail

When *Chocolate Dandies* closed in the spring of 1925, Josephine easily found work in the chorus line of the Plantation Club on Broadway where the star of the evening's entertainment was singer Ethel Waters. Josephine continued to develop her clowning and to step out of line to perform a speciality dance.

Ethel Waters was enjoying a big success singing 'Diana' among other numbers. Josephine assiduously learned all the songs and when Waters fell ill one day and could not appear, Josephine offered to go on in her place. Her rendering, if different, was appreciated – but not by the star, who made a rapid recovery and reappeared the very next evening.

During her appearance at the Plantation Club, an American socialite from Chicago, Caroline Dudley, came in with a jazz pianist, Spencer Williams. They were reportedly scouting for performers for a coloured revue Dudley was to take to Paris.

Dudley immediately fell for Josephine's antics and made her an offer of $150 a week to join the troupe she was forming. When Josephine hesitated, Dudley offered $200. When Josephine cannily said she would consider, Dudley increased her offer to $250 and Josephine finally accepted. It was the turning point in her life.

At nineteen, Josephine had already come a long way from home in St. Louis. From Broadway she was about to make her biggest leap into the unknown – from New York to Paris – with a new troupe and a white promoter she had just met. Without calculating the risks but banking on the advantages, she took the plunge.

Josephine joined Caroline Dudley and some twenty coloured artistes and musicians on the Cunard Liner *Berengaria* bound for France. As she was later to affirm, 'When the Statue of Liberty disappeared over the horizon, I knew I was free!'

She didn't even tell her second husband, or her family.

Chapter Four

The Folies Bergère and Chez Joséphine

Events began to move swiftly for Josephine from the moment she returned to Paris from Berlin in early 1926. In the following months she was filmed for the first time and made her first gramophone record; she opened her own cabaret-restaurant near Pigalle; and she met the man who was to be her companion and manager for the next ten years. She was also thrust for the first time in her career into the turmoil of rehearsals for a big Paris revue.

From the moment Josephine had signed a contract with Paul Derval the previous year to appear in a revue at the Folies Bergère, preparations had gone ahead for the opening of *La Folie du Jour*. Written by veteran revue author, Louis Lemarchand, with music by a dozen different composers, including Irving Berlin and Spencer Williams, *La Folie du Jour* was Derval's bid to rival the revues at the Moulin Rouge and the Casino de Paris, in which Mistinguett and Maurice Chevalier were the stars.

Derval saw in Josephine an artiste who could compete with older, established performers, if she were given the right opportunity and training. He reasoned that Josephine, who was thirty years younger than the celebrated Miss, possessed enough youthful vigour and self-assurance to compensate for her lack of experience in big Paris revues. Her innate talent and intelligence would enable her to reach the standard he had set for his leading artistes.

Paul Derval was a self-made man who had once been an actor and knew the theatre inside out. He saw the role of the Folies Bergère as responding to what he called the 'rule of pleasure', which he defined as the public's need to 'laugh and dream through a ceaseless blending of the emotions through illusion...' When he took over the Folies after the war he carried out a two-

76

year renovation programme that transformed what was then the oldest music hall in Paris into a veritable 'pleasure factory' which was the best equipped and most modern of its day.

The old 'winter garden' with its fountains and ferns at the entrance was replaced by a spacious foyer decorated with garishly coloured rococo plaster mouldings and huge ornate wooden chandeliers. Within the auditorium a second balcony was added; backstage installations included the famous portable staircase whose narrow treads were to intimidate so many famous artistes. Below the stage a warm water swimming pool was built which rose into view for special aquatic sequences.

Many of the older habitués never forgave Derval for doing away with the celebrated *promenoir*, or walking area, at the back of the stalls, where ladies of pleasure had been traditionally allowed to proposition their clients. Derval believed that the stage should have the undivided attention of the audience.

Together with his wife, Antonia, Paul Derval ran the Folies Bergère like an old established family business. From his panelled first-floor office he directed an army of 180 stagehands and electricians with an aloof paternalism, while Madame Derval, who was known amongst the staff as 'la marquise', supervised the backstage workshops and costume store. It was their belief that over-familiarity with the staff only led to demands for wage increases.

Derval left the auditioning of over one hundred chorus girls and models to his stage manager, reserving for himself the task of engaging his principal artistes. But despite being an astute businessman, Derval, like many theatre folk, retained a grain of irrational superstition about the theatre. From the time of his first success at the Folies, the titles of his revues always contained exactly thirteen letters and usually incorporated the word *Folie*. He collected enough unused thirteen-letter titles to last a hundred years and the tradition of the thirteen-letter title is maintained to this day.

Having acceded to Josephine's supplementary salary demand, transmitted from Berlin, Derval set about making the most of his investment. Appreciating Josephine's need for confidence in her new and exacting role, Derval announced to the press that she possessed the 'sacred fire' of a great artiste, and he began grooming her for the part. Josephine was installed in a rooming house a few steps from the main gates of the Parc Monceau, on the elegant west side of the capital. She was invited to go out and buy anything she wanted and charge the purchases to Monsieur Derval. As an initial gesture he bought her a puppy dog for company. The public image of Josephine Baker, future star of the Folies Bergère, began to take shape.

For her part, Josephine was content for the moment to put herself in the hands of someone old enough to be her father and who could further her career. She dutifully accepted Derval's directives and was glad to get back to work again. Her early training as a trouper in America enabled her to settle into the arduous routine of a costly and elaborate *revue à grand spectacle*.

The mid-Twenties was a formative period for Grand, or Spectacular, Revue. Managements in London, Paris, Berlin and New York vied with one another to present ever more elaborate productions and to engage the most celebrated international artistes to perform in them. The trend had started in London in 1920 when Charles Cochran staged *London, Paris and New York*. Cochran tried to sign up the notorious French murderer, Landru, for one of his revues, but the guillotine had a prior claim on him. Within two years Florence Mills and the Blackbirds had Londoner's singing 'I'm Just Wild About Harry' in the Broadway touring company of *Shuffle Along*, the all-black American revue in whose road tour company Josephine had danced at the age of sixteen, before coming to Europe.

By the early Twenties the friendly informality of the traditional music hall, with its master of ceremonies introducing a series of disconnected turns, had given way to 'revues', with a 'personality' as compère or commère to give a semblance of continuity to the bill. Revues were written around such artistes as Gaby Deslys, Mistinguett and Maurice Chevalier, whose personalities offered an underlying theme and whose presence provided a measure of artistic unity to the production.

By 1925 revue in France had developed into *revue à grand spectacle*, or Grand Revue, in which a large cast appeared in a series of elaborate scenes with special effects and a full orchestral accompaniment. The growing popularity of the cinema encouraged managements to offer the public what the flickering black and white screen could not provide – the living presence of a celebrity backed by a hundred or more supporting players, in a series of dazzlingly colourful tableaux.

There was no lack of choice of themes. Historical subjects were always popular; when Mistinguett played the part of the mistress of King Louis XV, Madame du Barry, who was guillotined, the execution scene was so realistic that the Préfecture de Police banned the performance. In London the same scene had merely provoked laughter.

In 1922 the Casino de Paris had offered an unhappy marriage between stage and screen when the management presented Pearl White, the silent screen heroine of adventure films, in person on the stage. In engaging her, the management expected some demonstrations of the fearlessness apparent in films, in which the young blonde woman clung to tall buildings or cliffs or hung from aeroplanes. But on arrival in Paris, Miss White confided that she had no head for heights and that doubles and trick photography had been used for her more sensational film sequences. The management resorted to showing a film clip of her arriving in Paris by air, before revealing her diminutive figure in person on the stage. Although she appeared on a high wire above the heads of the audience and was lassoed on the stage, she was put to no personal risk in her engagement.

The attempt to marry the two media was, however, a portent of the future when cinemas would literally invade the theatre and the then forty cinemas in Paris were to be multiplied many times over, even taking over such celebrated theatres as the Moulin Rouge and the Olympia.

With the advent of films with sound only months away, the staging of Grand Revue had become a costly and elaborate operation in which reputations and considerable investments were put at stake. Managements were obliged to engage internationally known artistes and their salaries were correspondingly high.

While the Parisian press complained of a decline in the standards of the Comédie Française, the French National

Repertory Theatre, some music hall artistes were commanding much higher fees than their colleagues in the legitimate theatre. The popular boulevard actor, Lucien Guitry, for example, was earning 1,500 francs a performance, while Mistinguett could claim 3,500 francs, plus a percentage of the box office receipts, every time she stepped on to the stage of the Moulin Rouge.

In a win or lose attempt to recoup his investment, Derval spared no trouble or expense in preparing his new revue, *La Folie du Jour* and grooming Josephine for the leading role. He was now paying her 27,000 francs a month and he was determined to get his money's worth. For nearly a year prior to the opening of *La Folie du Jour*, some five hundred people were involved in preparatory activities. Dancers and models were auditioned, production numbers planned and rehearsed, dances devised. Derval also believed in dressing his shows well. Some 1,500 costumes were designed, fitted and made under the supervision of Max Weldy, an international costumier.

Derval tried to exploit Josephine's origins and exotic image to the maximum. The author of the review, Louis Lemarchand, wrote scenes that would give full scope to her 'wild beauty' and provide a framework for her talents merely glimpsed in the *Revue Nègre*. Most of the chorus girls were light-skinned English blondes, whose complexion contrasted with Josephine's bronze colour. Years later, Derval remarked, 'In those days Josephine did not yet understand that the colour of her skin was an essential element of her personality.'

It was Derval who initiated the accessory that became Josephine's trademark – the girdle of bananas. The costume was created by Paul Poiret, the Parisian couturier, then at the height of his powers, who had designed clothes for Sarah Bernhardt and Mistinguett. Josephine's scanty costume was composed of sixteen artificial bananas studded with rhinestones and arranged in a girdle around her loins. For ever afterwards Josephine was to be associated with her bananas costume and the sensuality of the vision became a legend.

Many writers and critics have mistakenly affirmed that the bananas first appeared in the *Revue Nègre*. Recognising their symbolic value, Maurice Verne, a writer of the period, later claimed to have obtained the original celebrated girdle for his private museum of theatrical artefacts.

Although Josephine was an attentive pupil in Derval's hands, she was also self-willed and independent of nature. She began to show clear signs of distaste for the costume fittings and to rebel against the need to be present for discussions and rehearsals.

In an evident riposte to her supplementary salary demand, Derval had made it a contractual obligation for Josephine to be present when required. Derval had Paul Poiret create special gowns for Josephine, and accompanied her to fitting sessions. This was less out of solicitude for his protégée than to be sure she kept her appointment with Poiret. The couturier began by creating a robe for Josephine which he called 'Un Rien' (A Nothing). The bill was 9,000 francs! For Josephine it was all a far cry from the catch-all style of southern American tent shows and the shaky improvisations that had characterised preparations for the *Revue Nègre*.

Rehearsals for *La Folie du Jour* were not without incident. Derval had planned to have Josephine standing on a mirror in a large flowered globe which would descend from the roof of the auditorium to stop above the orchestra, when she would perform a dance.

During a rehearsal, one of the supporting cables stuck and the globe containing Josephine tilted alarmingly, threatening to send her crashing down into the orchestra pit. While some of the chorus looked on horrified and near to fainting, Josephine remained suspended and hung on calmly for long minutes until she was hauled to safety. Her physical toughness and courage had helped her through without panic. It was Maurice Chevalier who once said that music hall artistes are nearer to circus performers than to theatre actors.

Ever since she had come to prominence in the *Revue Nègre*, Paris audiences had been avid for another glimpse of Josephine. *La Folie du Jour* satisfied almost all their expectations. Her reappearance provoked another outpouring of adulation in the press. Columnists even tried to mimic her style of dancing by writing in staccato, disjointed phrases.

The English socialite, Nancy Cunard, who was collecting

material for her book on black culture, wrote in *Vogue* magazine of the 'perfect delight of Josephine Baker, most astounding of mulatto dancers, in her necklets, bracelets and flouncing feathered loincloths. The fuzz had been taken out of her hair, which shines like a dark blue crystal, as she yodels (the nearest thing one can get to expressing it) and contorts her surprising form through a maze of complicated rhythms'.

Another *Vogue* writer called Josephine 'a woman possessed, a savage intoxicated with tom-toms, a shining machine, a dancer, an animal, all joints and no bones... at one moment she is the fashion artists model, at the next Picasso's'.

Marcel Sauvage, poet and journalist for *l'Intransigeant* newspaper, wrote of the tremendous applause that greeted Josephine on opening night. In a vivid description of her performance headed *Comique Nudité de Bronze* he coined phrases that would be echoed many times by other writers in later years.

An eyewitness recalls, 'The curtain opened and a swing came out across the audience. And cackling like a monkey in a tree was this glorious creature with just a little bunch of bananas around her waist. As she swung back and forth, the house went to pieces. And I knew she was a work of art, a product of Paris and her own race!'

The high spot of *La Folie du Jour* was Josephine's descent from the ceiling of the theatre above the heads of the audience. The huge flower-encrusted globe was slowly lowered from the roof to stop just above the orchestra. It then slowly opened to reveal Josephine standing on a mirror, nude save for a string of bananas around her waist.

One observer wrote,

> The blue spotlight turned Josephine's tan body into a true café au lait colour. Her slicked-down hair looked as though it were painted with tar, and the bananas took on the brilliant yellow of a Cézanne painting.

Pierre de Régnier expressed shocked surprise in his printed column: 'Is she horrible? Is she Negro, is she white? Has she hair, or is her skull painted black? One hasn't time to find out...'

In his memoirs of music hall personalities, Louis Léon-Martin remembers how

> the orchestra struck up a Charleston and Josephine Baker, her
> lovely café au lait body suddenly dislocated, plunged into an
> agitated and frantic dance. She was really dancing five or six times
> at the same time, for the reflection of her legs in the mirror,
> thrown on the decor, on the boxes and on the ceiling with huge
> shadows, multiplied the fury of her steps... And yet, I could not
> seem to forget the young Bacchante who once swayed her hips in
> front of the simple oilcloth backdrop which draped the stage of
> the Champs-Élysées Theatre.

As she danced on the mirror, her grimacing and writhing made
the audience gasp. Then the globe slowly closed over her and the
apparition vanished. Josephine's 'high wire' act was not, however,
the first such novelty to be seen at the Folies. Agnès Souret had
crossed the auditorium throwing roses down on the upturned
faces of the audience in 1920.

As with the *Revue Nègre* there were some dissenting voices.
The sixty-seven-year-old Charles Maurice Donnay, poet and
member of the French Academy, a former cabaret performer,
who edited a news-sheet for the Chat Noir cabaret, wrote of 'an
impression of a nightmare in its awful monotony' and moaned
that 'the audience pay 35 and 40 francs a seat to see Negroes
dancing to discordant music...'

The sour notes of criticism of Josephine's performance were
quickly drowned out by praise from the press and public alike.
The world was no longer shocked by Josephine's behaviour and
she became an accepted part of the French music hall scene.

Josephine's bid for stardom at the Folies invited inevitable
comparison with her predecessors. In the eyes of Pierre
MacOrlan,

> Mistinguett represented the expression of an infinitely tragic
> subconscious, stylised for the music hall. Josephine, more than
> Miss, reveals to us an unconsciousness which crosses lines,
> disrupts our way of seeing things and reminds us of a primitive
> order. She embodies the soul of reaction. She laughs in the face
> of arteriosclerosis.

Georges Simenon and 'Count' Pepito

Since signing her contract with Paul Derval and breaking with Caroline Dudley, her original sponsor, Josephine had handled her own affairs. After her departure from the *Revue Nègre*, and her tearful farewell to Sydney Bechet who had accompanied her across the Atlantic, she found herself with new colleagues and her New York links severed for the first time since her arrival in Europe. But apart from her limited circle of theatrical acquaintances at the Folies she had no intimate friends and she began to feel very alone.

For the first time in her life, Josephine now had more money than she knew what to do with, but there were plenty of hangers-on ready to help her spend it. She began to indulge in frivolous purchases and also gave freely to those who pleaded personal misfortune. When it became known that she was an 'easy touch', the stage doorkeeper at the Folies frequently had to protect her from opportunists seeking a handout.

When the taxman began to make his inevitable demands on the star it seemed to Josephine that it was as unjust as it was incomprehensible that the State should seize so large a part of her hard-won earnings. It was the first sign of her incapacity to understand and handle her own finances. At such moments of confusion and loneliness, she sought comfort in the only living creatures she felt close to – her growing family of pets. At one moment her menagerie included two cats, two dogs, a goat, a rabbit, a parrot and a snake. Some of these creatures she managed to smuggle into her dressing room at the theatre, much to Paul Derval's annoyance.

If, for the moment, the stringent demands of her Folies engagement left Josephine with little time of her own, she lacked intimate friends to whom she could turn for companionship or advice. She did not lack for company; on the contrary, she was continually surrounded by people.

As the newest star of the Folies Bergère, Josephine's presence at social gatherings was constantly being solicited and her appearance at selected soirées was considered by Derval to be a necessary part of her public position as a *vedette*. There were social gatherings, all-night parties, and more formal events at which a hostess might think nothing of hiring teams of black waiters in outlandish oriental costumes to serve equally extravagantly attired guests. Such was the ingrown nature of the social milieu, revolving around the same nucleus of personalities, an exotic newcomer such as Josephine was clearly a curiosity to be cultivated.

Josephine was continually being introduced to talented and prominent personalities whose name and reputation were completely unknown to her. Her lack of knowledge of both the French language and culture made such meetings tedious and unsatisfying. Worse, she was completely unschooled in the social graces. Above all, she lacked the kind of male companionship a young woman of twenty usually seeks.

To compensate for her naivety and changed circumstances, Josephine began to indulge in excesses of behaviour. Misunderstanding the French term for snake skin (*peau de serpent*), she bought a real serpent. When she realised her mistake, she defiantly appeared with the reptile round her neck in public. It scared people so much she inadvertently achieved her objective of being talked about, and her extravagant gesture was taken to be the height of fashion.

Among her impulsive purchases, books seemed to Josephine to offer the knowledge and experience she lacked. 'Now I've got what I want,' she told her future first biographer, journalist Marcel Sauvage. 'A big dictionary in seven volumes full of pictures. I don't open it. I haven't time. When I weigh each volume it makes me laugh.'

In fact Josephine preferred reading crime fiction. As she read the stories of Edgar Wallace she carefully pressed between the pages petals of violets from bouquets from admirers.

Among the many men who sought Josephine offstage, one was a young Belgian journalist who offered to help her with her personal papers. He was also a prolific writer of popular fiction, using half a dozen different pen names for his novelettes. Georges Simenon was soon to begin to sign his own name to his detective stories featuring Commissaire Maigret.

It has been said that Simenon became Josephine's paid secretary. This has been denied by his first wife, Régine Renchon, who agreed that 'for a few weeks Simenon helped Josephine, when she was between managers, to set her papers and accounts into some kind of order. But that was all. He merely helped her as a friend. Josephine Baker was not exactly a businesswoman'.

But it was not all, as Régine Renchon later admitted. 'Of course Simenon was Josephine's lover,' she told the biographer, Fenton Bresher. 'I have learnt it since, but I was ignorant of it at the time.'

Few doubt that what Régine Renchon said was true. Simenon was a self-proclaimed hedonist for whom nothing was more splendid than a woman's body and he boasted about his conquests. At the time of his meeting with Josephine he was contributing articles on black Africans and declaring that, for him, 'colour prejudice did not exist.' He never defined his sexual relationship with Josephine, possibly because it seemed so obvious as to be unnecessary.

In his autobiographical work, *Mémoires Intimes*, Simenon says of Josephine, 'If I refused to marry her it was because, being an unknown, I didn't want to become Mr Baker.' He adds that he took refuge on the island of Aix with his first wife in order to forget Josephine. A young black servant in the Simenon household in Connecticut, USA, later recalled that 'Josephine Baker was a big part of his life and he talked about her a lot'. After meeting Josephine in New York, many years later, Simenon admitted, 'We were still as in love with each other.'

It was at this moment in her life that the man who was to become Josephine's closest companion for the next ten years appeared on the scene. Pepito Abatino was introduced to Josephine one afternoon at a watering hole in Montmartre called Joe Zelli's. An Italian caricaturist who frequented the establishment greeted her and presented '...My cousin, Giuseppi Abatino, recently arrived from Rome'.

Paris at that period was teeming with talented immigrants whose source of income often was the growing influx of tourists, many from across the Atlantic, who took advantage of a favourable rate of exchange for their dollars. The resident immigrants were ready to assume any guise and perform any service to satisfy the expectations of visitors eager to plunge into the artistic and intellectual life of the capital. Exiled Russian princes became taxi drivers, and counts and *clochards* were indistinguishable at the café tables of Montmartre and Montparnasse. Paris offered a backcloth against which all could play out their fantasies and invent new identities for themselves.

Pepito Abatino was a tall, elegant Italian of obscure origin who had been spending his time in Paris chaperoning American women tourists and perfecting his own dance technique at the same time. Joe Zelli's was a natural meeting place for expatriate Americans and those moving on the fringe of the artistic milieu.

The tango was enjoying a vogue at the time. Rudolf Valentino was celebrated as the 'great screen lover' of the silent screen. If Pepito did not have Valentino's looks (he resembled more another film actor of the day, Adolf Menjou), he could dance an impressive tango. Screwing his monocle into position and announcing that he was Count Pepito de Abatino, a descendant of a noble Sicilian family with ministerial connections in Rome, Pepito went into action.

Josephine said later that it was not his claim to aristocratic lineage but the way Pepito danced the tango that seduced her. In her eyes Pepito combined the elegance and social class to which she aspired. From their first encounter on the dance floor, Josephine and Pepito were inseparable.

When Pepito was seen constantly in Josephine's company there was immediate speculation that a marriage, possibly in secret, was imminent. While the popular press began to write freely about 'Prince Abatino and the Black Contessa', most observers simply regarded them as lovers. Some who observed Josephine's rise as an artiste deplored the way she had fallen for someone they called a 'tea-dance gigolo'.

A prominent female personality in Montmartre at this time was a black entertainer named Bricktop, who sang at Le Grand Duc, a club in the Rue Pigalle. An astute observer of human nature and friend and confidante of such celebrities as Cole Porter, Scott Fitzgerald and visiting black artistes, Bricktop, or Ada Smith Ducongé, was unequivocal about Pepito. She called him a 'bum who couldn't even pay for a glass of beer, who took over, flattered Josephine and followed her around like a puppy, but had a sharp business know-how...'

Pepito already had the makings of a public relations agent, before such an occupation became recognised as part of star billing, and he set about selling his protégée to the public. He organised sponsorship of chosen commercial products and demanded a fee for Josephine's published endorsement. She thus lent her name to Vitus portable radios, the drink marketed as Pernod, Bakerfix ('The secret of my hairstyle') and a metallic home exercising machine.

Pepito also published a book of collected newspaper cuttings containing more than one hundred appreciative comments of Josephine's performances. The preface to the book claimed it contained 'all the hidden qualities that Josephine's shy nature didn't want revealed'.

Josephine's qualities were already being fully appreciated by Georges Simenon, who, as Pepito's rival for her favours, promptly sat down and produced *Josephine Baker's Magazine*, an editorial tour de force containing Josephine's own comments, sketches of her by Paul Colin, and articles on jazz, food, fashion and boxing. Typical of Josephine's wisdom were remarks like, 'I like people I don't know well, because I haven't the time to discover their defects. But I also like those I know because I have the time to discover their qualities.' For all the galaxy of contributors, the brilliantly planned magazine never appeared on the news stands. The designs for the first two issues are kept at the Simenon Foundation in Liège.

A vivid souvenir of Josephine, Simenon and Pepito in Paris in 1927 exists in a photograph of them sitting together in a mirrored bar with champagne and sandwiches in front of them. A youthful, smiling Simenon turns to Josephine and her companion as she clowns by crossing her eyes. Sitting protectively close to Josephine, Pepito grins sheepishly at the camera. In their comparatively relaxed behaviour, Josephine and Simenon seem to be sure of themselves and their respective futures. Pepito, seventeen years Josephine's senior, would remain at her side for only the few short years left to him. She was still only twenty-one.

Chez Joséphine

In December 1926, on the advice of Pepito Abatino who had taken all her affairs in hand, Josephine opened her own nightclub called Chez Joséphine at No. 40 Rue Fontaine near the Place Pigalle. The decision was taken after they had abandoned several establishments in Montmartre, such as the Imperial, the Milonga and the Abbaye de Thélème, at which Josephine had been accustomed to dance after her evening appearance at the Folies. The extra business she attracted everywhere she went in public persuaded Pepito that it would be profitable to open a place of their own.

Such was Josephine's drawing power that the owner of one nightclub in Montmartre demanded 300,000 francs damages for alleged breach of contract. When Josephine opened her own establishment, jealous tongues said that Montmartre had 'at last found its real black cat', an allusion to Le Chat Noir, the Montmartre nightclub that had flourished in the late nineteenth century.

Chez Joséphine was partly inspired by the success of Le Boeuf sur le Toit, the nightclub named after a ballet of the same name devised by Jean Cocteau, which had a reputation of offering the 'wildest fantasy within the finest of established traditions'. In the five years of its existence, Le Boeuf had in fact become the habitual meeting place of an artistic and intellectual elite, which included the celebrated 'Six'* composers and many of Cocteau's friends.

An oddly matched duo, Wiéner and Doucet, improvised on two pianos while young Cocteau occasionally accompanied them on a small drum set. From time to time Wiéner and Doucet left their home patch at Le Boeuf to play at Chez Joséphine. Casting his mind back to that period in the late Seventies, Jean Wiéner told the author that he found the atmosphere at Chez Joséphine to be *mondaine*, with fashionable Parisians and rich tourists forming the majority of customers. He remembered that Chez

---

* The Six included Georges Auric, Louis Durey, Arthur Honegger, Darius Milhaud, Francis Poulenc and Germaine Tailleferre. Their self-appointed spokesman was Jean Cocteau.

Joséphine was more popular and less intellectual than Le Boeuf sur le Toit.

Chez Joséphine suffered from none of the pretentiousness to be found at Le Boeuf, and was unashamedly dedicated to pleasure and frivolity. 'I want people to jump around and shake off their worries like a dog shaking off its fleas,' said Josephine as she opened up her new club.

Partly because she did not know who they were or what they represented in Paris life, Josephine was quite unabashed by the celebrities she received and she treated everyone with the same familiarity. Pepito saw to it that the more important customers were invited to sign the 'Golden Book', which soon contained the signatures of Jean Cocteau and Georges Auric (Le Boeuf habitués), the cineaste René Clair, the poet Robert Desnos, not to mention such foreign personalities as Count Herman de Keyserling, philosopher and founder of the 'École de la Sagesse'.

Josephine also remembers receiving Picasso, accompanied by film actor villain Gaston Modot and poet Blaise Cendrars. To Mario Nalpas, the Greek film director friend of Cendrars, Josephine said how much she would have liked to have been in his film *Sultane de l'Amour*, which had been photographed at his villa at Cimiez. When Modot, who had appeared in the film, spoke of the 'family atmosphere' that existed amongst those making the film, Josephine replied regretfully, 'Not like the music hall where one only meets in the evening...'

It was at this time that Josephine's outgoing manner made her a natural subject for film makers. Lights were set up in the Saulnier Passage next to the Folies Bergère and, watched by curious onlookers, she was invited to perform the Charleston in front of a hand-cranked camera. Mario Nalpas advised not to look directly into the arc lamps and with no one to advise her how to act she blindly performed the same steps, in the same make-up, as she did every night in the theatre, while the operator turned the handle.

The exercise was later repeated in a longer silent version directed by Nalpas. The resulting film, *La Revue des Revues*, was in Josephine's opinion 'a horror!' Despite her initial disillusionment with the cinema, Josephine was soon to make her first full-length feature film with Nalpas. A fraternity of pioneer film makers was emerging in Paris. Mario Nalpas's cousin, Louis, was one of Abel Gance's seven collaborators on the celebrated *Napoléon* film, premiered at the Paris Opera on 7 April 1927.

Josephine found the film actors who visited her in her club less attractive in the flesh than their screen images. 'Everyone has two arms, two legs, a stomach and a head. Everyone does what he can…' she fatuously proclaimed as she plied the customers with champagne. The kitchen catered for their stomachs and the general atmosphere of relaxed informality helped customers not to worry their heads too much about the bill.

Although Josephine liked to refer to her nightclub as a 'bistro', with all the modesty that implied, the menu offered at Chez Joséphine was one of the most expensive in Paris. Oysters were 45 francs a dozen, caviar was 40 francs a portion, twice what it cost to eat a full meal at Le Boeuf. Merely to reserve a table in advance was 40 francs. It was Pepito's belief that all who wanted a closer look at the Black Venus should pay well for the privilege.

Josephine put all her considerable surplus energy into her new enterprise and was the life and soul of the nightly gatherings at Chez Joséphine. Sweeping in a few moments after her last curtain call at the Folies which was conveniently situated just down the road, she would be greeted with fresh applause from customers seated at the tables. When she told them that the live pig kept in the kitchen was called Albert, 'after my "maître d'hôtel", a good man', there would be a gust of laughter and the night would be off to a promising start. An early sign of high spirits to come would be when, after the first glass of champagne, normally reserved customers would start batting balls of paper across the room with rackets thoughtfully supplied by the management.

In exchange for their patronage, Josephine gave customers advice on how to dance the Charleston, the Black Bottom and the Cakewalk. The highlight of an evening spent at Chez Joséphine was a demonstration of these dances by Josephine, followed by more or less successful attempts by the customers to imitate her loose-limbed gyrations. They were told that such dances were not exclusively concerned with the legs and feet and that the hands and arms also played an important part.

'The Charleston should be danced wearing necklaces of shells which jump about on your skin and make a dry sound,' Josephine would tell the company. 'It's a matter of dancing with your hips, from one to the other, and sticking out your bottom and shaking your hands. For some time bottoms have been hidden too much. They exist. I don't see what's wrong with them. It's true that some bottoms are silly, so pretentious and so insignificant. They are only good for sitting on – if that!'

If this view led her listeners to believe that the name of the Black Bottom dance referred to the human anatomy, no one was likely to correct that erroneous idea. The name simply indicated the muddy black bottom of the Mississippi, along which the black slave dances from Africa made their way northwards from New Orleans.

As the band struck up, tipsy customers would get to their feet and, forgetting their pride, stick out their posteriors and shake their hands in the air to the rhythm of the Charleston played by a small group of musicians. The similarity between their movements and those of the tribal dance of the Ibos of West Africa would possibly have surprised them, had they known the pedigree of black American dances. They would have been equally surprised to learn that bodily contact in such ritualistic dances was excluded by their African originators.

It was also on such high-spirited occasions that Josephine could often be persuaded to sing. With musical accompaniment she would intone in a slightly nasal voice a well-known Negro spiritual or the words of one of her first recordings of 'Who' or 'That Certain Feeling'. The way she made the word *toujours* rhyme with *amour* in the French version of Irving Berlin's 'Always' brought wild applause and promises to buy her latest records the very next day. She would then disappear into the kitchen, as though leaving the stage, to feed her pet goat, Toutoute, with milk from a baby's bottle.

One visitor who came to take a long, friendly look at Josephine, was the novelist Colette, whose latest book, *La fin de Chéri*, had helped to establish her as a writer of some consequence. The meeting went beyond the ritual exchange of pleasantries, according to Josephine. Remembering her own experiences as a music hall artiste Colette may have found in Josephine a kindred spirit who had the same survival instincts as herself. There was an unspoken affinity between them and their friendship was to endure.

As an exercise in public relations, Chez Joséphine was a success. It enabled Josephine, who appeared to have an inexhaustible fund of energy and needed constant company, to play hostess at her own table and have her guests pay for the experience. Accompanied by Pepito she would return home at dawn after having performed the previous evening at the Folies, then making an appearance at her nightclub followed, perhaps, by a visit to an all-night private party. Everywhere she went she found a welcome. As Josephine later recalled, 'I never enjoyed myself so much. I played jokes, stroked the heads of bald men, pulled their beards and made fat women dance!'

The First Record

If Pepito had begun by selling himself to Josephine, he quickly began turning his talents to selling her. One of the first things Pepito did was to encourage Josephine to sing. Ever since her disastrous attempts in front of the passengers on board the liner that brought her to Europe, Josephine had yearned to sing again, but was afraid to do so. Under studio recording conditions she began to develop her singing voice.

Josephine's ascension as an artiste coincided with the commercial development of electrical recording and the rapid proliferation of recording companies. Mass-produced shellac records of dance music and jazz were available in Europe and America at an easily affordable price.

In September 1926, the French Odéon record company had invited Josephine to record for the first time. Among the six sides cut, 'That Certain Feeling' by George Gershwin (Odéon 49.171). is considered a rarity. Her first record was a sentimental foxtrot, 'Who' by Hammerstein, Harbach and Kern, from the American musical comedy, *Sunny*, which had opened the previous year in New York at the New Amsterdam Theatre, almost on the day that Josephine had sailed for Europe. Unfortunately, Claude Hopkins and his band, who had played in the *Revue Nègre*, had returned to

New York and Josephine was poorly accompanied in her very first recording by the Seven Fox Blues Charleston Jazz Band, led by Maestro Olivier. When news circulated that Josephine Baker's records were available, Mistinguett promptly recorded a French language version of 'Who' entitled '*Qui*'.

Josephine's first recordings for the Odéon label had already revealed her potential as a singer, but she was still mainly thought of as a dancer. It was as a dancer and star of the Folies Bergère that Josephine appeared before President Poincaré at the fashionable charity event, *Le Bal des Petits Lits Blancs*, held at the Opéra. When she danced on the traditional *Pont d'Argent* and identified the President from his little white goatee beard, watching the proceedings from his box, she kicked her legs a little higher and remained convinced that he laughed at her in acknowledgement.

Josephine also appeared for one night at the *Bal Nègre*, organised by Paul Colin, who, since his association with Josephine and the *Revue Nègre*, had remained attracted by black music and dance. Her appearance at the *Bal Nègre*, and the poster Colin produced for the event, reminded many of Josephine's sensational debut in Paris eighteen months before.

Josephine's celebrity was the cause of an incident which greatly perturbed a young singer when they appeared on the same bill at a theatre in Nice. The owner of the theatre, Marcel Sablon, had engaged Josephine as the main attraction in a programme that also included his brother, Jean, who was at the beginning of his singing career. As the star of the Folies Bergère on her first visit to the Côte d'Azur, Josephine was clearly the main attraction of the programme and as such she was accorded the most important, second half of the bill. Jean Sablon appeared in the first half of the programme, supported by André Ekyan and the gypsy guitarist, Django Reinhardt.

Reinhardt opened the programme with a solo rendering of 'St. Louis Blues', after which Sablon began to sing a series of well-chosen songs. He was a meticulous performer who required total attention from an audience. Spectators who had come to see Josephine grew restive and began to raise their voices. Sablon's performance ended amid whistles and shouting and he left the stage shaken by the experience, convinced that his light, caressing style of singing had been totally unappreciated by the audience.

Josephine and Pepito immediately went to his dressing room to console him. Josephine said, 'It's nothing. It has happened to me and it's nothing at all, you'll see.'

For Sablon, still at the stage where he was developing his style, the incident remained a painful memory and contributed to his sensitivity concerning the conditions for his song recitals. Years later, his nationwide following in the United States was achieved with a skilful microphone technique in which no interference was possible and with sound technicians and listeners who offered him their undivided attention.

The First Biography

It was at this time that the first attempt to capture the Black Venus within the covers of a book was made. The journalist and poet, Marcel Sauvage, who had hurried back to Paris from Marseilles two years earlier when he had read about the *Revue Nègre*, began a series of interviews with her for the Paris evening newspaper, *l'Intransigeant*.

At first Sauvage was obliged to call upon the services of an interpreter since neither he nor Josephine could speak each other's language.

'I am a dancer! I dance!' exclaimed Josephine, 'Write my memoirs! I live in the present! *Now*!' And she stabbed a finger in the direction of the floor to indicate the present in sign language.

When Marcel Sauvage first informed his editor of his intention to write Josephine's biography, he was told, 'You are mad to want to write the memoirs of a twenty-year-old girl.' And when Sauvage put his first question to Josephine, she simply giggled and said, 'Mémoires...? Mais je ne me souviens pas encore de mes souvenirs. Attendez...!' (But I don't yet recall my memories...) There followed a stream of haphazard anecdotes and observations which were as unpredictable as Josephine's behaviour.

Les Mémoires de Joséphine Baker contained random notes on her early life, recent appearances in Paris and Berlin, cooking recipes, health and beauty notes, translations into French of several Negro songs, and a sample of her voluminous fan mail.

Her advice on health was a mixture of common sense and homespun philosophy. Thus:

> The best eau de toilette is rain water. It keeps indefinitely. A woman who takes care of her skin must have a cellar well stocked with bottles of rain water… Make-up should be liberally applied and must be frank. If not, it's deceit for those who are ill. Don't do it by halves… Dance as much as possible and sweat a lot. Sleep clears the eyes. Sleep completely nude under the bedclothes.

There was also earnest advice to take baths in milk of violets as well as steam baths every month – indulgences that were undreamed of by Josephine only a few years before, and unknown to many French women.

Les Mémoires de Joséphine Baker also contained thirty black and white drawings by Paul Colin, including a number of portraits of Josephine and imaginative sketches inspired by the tales she had told Marcel Sauvage. Whether by intention or coincidence, this first book about the youngest black American artiste to be fêted in Paris was published on the Fourth of July, American Independence Day, 1927. Sauvage's biography went into several editions and was later translated into eleven languages.

Josephine's popularity with the public can be judged from the fact that four days after her twenty-first birthday in June, crowds gathered at six o'clock in the morning near the Arc de Triomphe, in the fashionable sixteenth district of Paris, to watch her take her driving test. As Josephine puttered into the Avenue de la Grande Armée, in her brand new Voisin cabriolet with its shiny snake skin upholstery – a gift from an admirer named Monsieur Donnet – the well-wishers gathered at the kerbside received a wave from her elegantly gloved hand as though she was a member of the minor royalty. She had captured the interest of Parisians in her private life, and, needless to say, she obtained her first driving licence.

Journalists present took the opportunity of asking Josephine about Pepito, who was at her side. Were they married? Did they intend to get married? Did they have any plans for the future?

As people sought vainly for evidence of an official engagement, Josephine and Pepito did nothing to refute rumours that they were already secretly married. One newspaper gleefully reported, 'Countess Josephine has obtained her first driving licence!' Another paper, more daring, reported her as saying, 'I'm only twenty-one. It's the first time I am married. I don't know what I should do.' But this is thought to be pure invention.

It was not until a translation of Marcel Sauvage's biography appeared in Italy that news came back that Pepito was no nobleman, but a simple Sicilian citizen. Whether Josephine knew or suspected his true identity, she had no good reason to refuse his attentions and protection. In devoting himself to Josephine's increasingly diverse business affairs, his management skills were beginning to show dividends.

Her public appearances outside her regular performance at the Folies Bergère were carefully stage-managed by Pepito to promote her image in the eyes of the public. The many requests she received to give testimonials for commercial products were carefully examined, and only those considered in keeping with her image as a fashionable, healthy young woman were accepted.

Josephine gave her name to a hair preparation called 'Bakerfix' which allowed women to copy her slicked-down hairstyle. Black lipstick and coloured nail varnish enjoyed a new vogue, and kohl was used to emphasise the eyes.

Many women wanted to look like Josephine, at least as far as skin colour was concerned. If black was not yet 'beautiful' to everyone, Josephine's creamy café au lait skin colour seemed to many to possess the best of both the black and the white world. The new fashion of sunbathing allowed many the excuse to try to attain Josephine's bronze colour. Some women painted their skins with diluted iodine to keep their 'tan' all the year round. Others used artificial tanning preparations.

At the end of her advice on beauty in Marcel Sauvage's book, Josephine is quoted as saying, 'They wanted to make me out to be blacker than I am, but I don't want to be either whiter or blacker.' But while a whole generation of young women was trying to darken their skins to look different, if not more seductive, in the seclusion of her home Josephine was secretly swabbing herself each day with lemon juice in an effort to lighten her skin colour.

When she sat with closed eyes in Antoine's Salon de Coiffure while the hairstylist practised his art on her well-shaped head, or allowed Paul Poiret to indulge his sartorial creativity on her figure, it might have seemed to Josephine that Paris had wrought a greater transformation on her than could ever have been achieved by the rabbit's paw she kept as a fetish under her pillow at night. This modern magic owed nothing to African sorcerers or to the stories told to her by her great-aunt Elvira in St. Louis; it owed everything to Paris. Mistinguett expressed the feeling felt by many when she sang '*Ça c'est Paris*' ('Paris is like that').

Her First Feature Film

Josephine's growing notoriety encouraged Mario Nalpas to cast her in her first full-length feature film. *La Sirène des Tropiques*, based on a scenario by the novelist, Maurice Dekobra, tells the story of Papitou, a West Indian, who stows away on a ship to France to fulfil her dream of going on the stage. It was a thinly disguised version of Josephine's arrival in Europe and rise to stardom.

Josephine, as Papitou, performed with Georges Melchoir (of Jacques Feyder's celebrated desert saga, *L'Atlantide*), and Pierre Batcheff. Joe Alex appeared briefly with his large German sheepdog as Josephine's pet companion. Mario Nalpas and Henri Etiévant directed. A twenty-eight-year-old Spanish assistant was one of the team at the start of his own career as a film director... Luis Buñuel!

This silent film was largely improvised and Josephine was required to clown in a demeaning manner in a series of slapstick cameos. On the boat that brings Papitou to Europe she tumbles into a coal bunker and emerges jet black. She then falls into a flour bin and frightens an elderly passenger with her whiteness. The film ends, however, with Papitou's triumphant appearance on the stage of the Mogador Theatre in Paris.

Josephine felt humiliated by the character she portrayed and the inept way she had been directed. The film exploited her colour and clowning without offering her the opportunity to act. She was denied access to the scenario and simply photographed scene by scene. The experience left her disappointed and she reproached herself for having accepted the role. But she confided to her biographer, Marcel Sauvage, 'My greatest wish is to play in a big, beautiful and true film, because, for me, the cinema is nature and nothing but the truth.'

Jo Alex came to see Josephine at the Folies Bergère to suggest forming a black film company of artistes in Paris. It was to be called *Noir Film*. Despite initial enthusiasm it got no further. Pepito was not in favour, possibly fearing loss of influence over Josephine's career.

The *Spirit of St. Louis*

As the months passed Josephine settled into the role of *vedette* at the Folies Bergère and *patronne* of Chez Joséphine. Conforming to Derval's superstitious practice of maintaining a revue title containing thirteen letters and incorporating the word 'Folie', author Louis Lemarchand updated his 'hyper-revue' and in 1927 *La Folie du Jour* became *Un Vent de Folie*.

As Josephine's popularity continued to rise she found herself increasingly in demand, either for social events or by those seeking her collaboration in various projects. Journalists sought her out for their gossip columns but seldom troubled to ask more than her age and what she ate to keep her figure. While she was still mainly thought of as a dancer, her strident, slightly nasal voice on records began to fill many a home far away from the capital. The gramophone was still more acceptable than the static-ridden voices emanating from radio transmissions.

At home in Ménilmontant, Josephine was awakened each afternoon at about four o'clock when she almost always had a rendezvous or received a journalist. Often she would make a hasty appointment for a manicure or a pedicure, and then linger over some phials of expensive perfume or displays of exotic bracelets, before going on to the theatre. When, as was often the case, she arrived late, she would find Paul Derval, his Creole secretary Willie, the stage manager and her dresser, all in a state of panic. The 2,000 seat theatre would be full, and to cancel her appearance would entail huge trouble and expense.

On one memorable occasion, Josephine disappeared for several days without telling anyone where she was. Her doctor had refused to issue a medical certificate for her to rest without seeing her personally. Under stress and fatigue she simply left for the country. An understudy had taken her place at the last moment but the effect on the box office nearly caused the revue to close.

Historic Arrival

If clattering automobiles were beginning to fill the streets of Paris to a point where people complained of traffic congestion, the skies above France remained relatively free of machines, and the sight and sound of an aeroplane was cause for comment. When the American aviator Charles Lindbergh made his successful solo flight across the Atlantic from New York to Paris on 22 May 1927, it was a one-night special that 'stole the show' from the world of make-believe and challenged all previous ideas of time, distance and endurance.

With fuel running low, Lindbergh followed the course of the River Seine to Paris, where he circled the city searching for Le Bourget airfield. To the crowds scanning the night sky at ten o'clock, his tiny single-engine plane was barely visible. When he landed all Paris seemed to be there to greet him as they surged onto the runway. It had taken the twenty-five-year-old pilot exactly 33 hours and 29 minutes to fly 3,600 miles non-stop.

When reports of Lindbergh's arrival reached the Folies Bergère, Josephine was in her dressing room. On being told the news, she immediately rushed on to the stage and stopped the show. There was a breathless pause as she announced in a voice charged with emotion, 'Ladies and gentlemen! I have good news! Charles Lindbergh has arrived!'

As pandemonium broke loose, with people standing on their seats cheering, Josephine stood alone in the centre of the stage with tears of emotion streaming down her face. When the fragile aircraft called the *Spirit of St. Louis* landed in France, it was as though a small part of her home town had come to join her in Paris.

First World Tour

In 1928, Josephine and her manager, Pepito Abatino set out to conquer Europe and Latin America. In a marathon tour with *The Black and White Revue*, lasting two years, they visited more than a dozen countries and fulfilled scores of engagements in different cities and towns.

Reactions to Josephine's stage appearances differed widely. In most European capitals her fame had preceded her and the troupe was welcomed for bringing a taste of Parisian entertainment. In other centres on their itinerary, whole populations turned out to greet the arrival from Paris of the celebrated 'Black Venus'. People who had never before seen a black artiste, or heard American jazz, queued up out of curiosity. In some cities there were outbreaks of violent hostility to Josephine's reputedly immodest behaviour both on and off the stage.

Away from the tolerant atmosphere of Paris, where novelty and even eccentricity were the norm, Josephine was once again exposed to the risks of racial and colour prejudice, and the touring revue sometimes became the victim of local religious and political pressures.

From the moment they left Paris, Josephine displayed a childlike curiosity in everything she saw. She eagerly compared each new city with Paris and every new country with what little she knew of France. Thus, she observed, the Dutch took their pleasures seriously and ate well... the policemen in The Hague wore white gloves that reminded her of Negro comics back home in America... Scandinavian countries appeared to be clean and the inhabitants correct in their behaviour... In Vienna, the River Danube was far less blue than the Seine! Behind the grandiose avenues and facades in South American cities she saw signs of poverty and hunger that reminded her of places she had known in the United States.

If Josephine was not already known to be the star of the Folies Bergère, she was nevertheless assured of maximum attention wherever she went, thanks to Pepito's dedication and flair for public relations. He knew that after viewing Josephine on the stage many people would not be content until they had seen her at close quarters. Experience in her club in Paris had proved that, in the right surroundings, closer contact with the customers paid off.

Through negotiations with the owners of local nightclubs and cabarets, Pepito had arranged for Josephine to be almost constantly on view to as many people as possible in each new city they visited. After each stage appearance, Josephine would be engaged to visit a chosen cabaret or club to 'dance, sing and amuse the customers', as the contract stipulated. Even in the streets the numberless brief encounters with passers-by helped to lay the groundwork for her future career for years to come. The routine was tiring, but profitable. Pepito had done his work well.

Most non-French audiences who saw Josephine on tour for the first time were won over by her energy and exuberance, and echoed the judgement of Paris. But not all cities were as welcoming as Paris and Berlin had been. The smaller the town in which she was billed to appear, the greater the sensation she provoked. If her scanty attire, including the now celebrated girdle of bananas, caused protests in some quarters, it was a measure of her ability to be liked and accepted by the public that the press affectionately announced the arrival of 'Joséfina, Koséfina, Giuseppina, Phifine, Pepel or La Bakerova...' depending on the language of the country visited. And while photographers fiddled with their cumbersome cameras, Josephine learned to be patient and hold the smile that became one of her trademarks.

If success seemed sometimes to come a little too easily, there were occasions when Josephine's announced arrival produced the opposite of a welcome, and Pepito was hard-pressed to defend her status as a serious performer. Such dedication was of no avail in Munich where the authorities flatly forbade Josephine to dance in public, justifying the interdiction with the assertion that 'Munich is a city with self-respect'. Josephine was banned from the stage for what was described as 'indecent behaviour'. The company was reduced to visiting the municipal museums to pass the time.

In Prague, by contrast, *The Black and White Revue* was given a tumultuous welcome at the railway station by many who recalled an earlier importation of Negro entertainment. An all-black revue called *The Chocolate Kiddies* had appeared three years earlier and was remembered for its 'wild, barbaric music, flamboyant costumes and snappy dance tunes'. The Czech press had hailed the troupe as 'wild Africa with all its colours and startling music brought by way of America to Europe'. The Prague public was apparently eager for more.

It was in Vienna that Josephine and Pepito came up against the harsh realities of post-war Europe. Since the break-up of the Austrian Empire the small, overcrowded capital of two million inhabitants was in a state of political unrest. Vienna was politically socialist but surrounded by provinces dominated by the church and reactionary elements were resisting change. Foreign influences were suspect and freedom of artistic expression became the target of Nationalist Party extremists. American jazz imported by Negroes was condemned in the name of racial purity. The first rumblings of fascism could be discerned.

The announcement of Josephine's imminent arrival in Vienna signalled the start of a violent campaign of protests against her appearance. The deputy representing the half-million Czechs in the country launched a campaign against what was called the 'moral decadence' that threatened the country and of which Josephine and her troupe were the agents. Four political parties called on the government to prohibit Josephine's appearance in the capital. Some of their supporters evoked memories of the visit of the American dancer, Isadora Duncan, who had scandalised the country a few years earlier with her near-nude performances.

Many Viennese has already been irritated by the jazz opera *Johnny Plays Up*, or *Johnny Spielt Auf*, which featured a Negro jazz musician. (The composer, Ernst Krenek, later fled Nazi Germany and emigrated to the United States).

At the eleventh hour before Josephine's arrival, the municipal senate refused to grant the Ronacher Theatre the necessary official permit for *The Black and White Revue* to appear. A group of nationalist and clerical deputies raised objections to Josephine's appearance in public on the grounds that nude dances endangered public morals. Extreme nationalist radicals even went so far as to speak of a *Negerschmach*, or the insult it would mean to the white population of the city if Josephine were allowed to appear on the stage. The local tour agents who had booked the Ronacher Theatre were forced to back down and dismiss the technical staff they had engaged. They still pursued play dates for her to appear in Berlin and Budapest.

While the church bells in Vienna called the faithful to worship on the weekend before the troupe's arrival, tracts were distributed in the streets condemning Josephine's performance as the 'work of the devil'. At divine service in Saint Peter's Church, opposite the Johann Strauss Theatre, where she was finally billed to appear, Capuchin and Jesuit priests preached sermons against Josephine as a 'symbol of an epoch of sin'. They warned their congregations against what they called 'white Negroes' – Europeans who emulated blacks by dancing the Charleston. The Jesuit, Father Frey, berated Josephine as the 'incarnation of lewdness, a black demon and a heretic personified'. For all that, when Josephine and the company had arrived in Vienna, they were greeted by an enthusiastic crowd in front of the Grand Hotel where they were booked to stay.

Many who attended church and heard public condemnation of *The Black and White Revue* went to see it anyway, and were relieved, if not delighted, when Josephine appeared in a full-length evening gown and sang a Negro lullaby entitled 'Pretty Little Baby', before breaking into her customary dance routine. For the government struggling against the effects of inflation and unemployment, the parade of luxurious Paris fashions which was included in the show was merely an added irritant. After her performance Josephine fulfilled a contract to dance at the fashionable Wolf Pavilion nightclub.

While the public took her to its heart, it remained for an eminent diplomat, Count Adelbert Steinberg, to redress the balance of official opinion. In a speech to the Austrian Upper House he castigated as hypocrites those who pretended to condemn feminine nudity on the stage while enjoying it in secret. Pressing his argument further he reminded his listeners that the most daring painted nudes in the world are to be seen in Saint Peter's in Rome, the Cathedral of the Pope.

As Josephine's audiences multiplied, so too did the possibility of unexpected incidents that even Pepito could not foresee. The man who hired the open-air Scarabus Theatre in Bucharest risked financial ruin if it rained before the first half of the programme; he would be contractually obliged to refund the cost of half the 1,700 seats. Josephine's one-night stand was already a sell-out when three thousand people turned up.

With thunder in the air on the night, the first large drops of rain fell as Josephine made her entrance. Up went the umbrellas as seats began to empty. The promoter was almost in tears. As the deluge intensified to torrential proportions, Josephine discarded her own umbrella and decided to continue her own performance, come what may. With her make-up running, her costume soaked, the orchestra responded, albeit damply, to a conductor holding his umbrella in one hand. People who had been left out quickly bought up the vacated seats. The show ended in triumph over adversity, for audience, musicians and players alike. Josephine had demonstrated the true meaning of the word 'trouper' and the nervous backer recouped his investment.

A different kind of deluge fell on Josephine in Prague. When Josephine appeared at the vast underground Lucerna Theatre she was showered with hundreds of rabbit's paws, thrown on the stage by a delirious audience who had read about her fetish for rabbit's paws. The readiness of the public to respond to her whims touched Josephine deeply.

The Czech cinema publication, *World of Moving Pictures*, dated 14 April 1928, devoted almost its entire issue to Josephine, and another young artiste at the beginning of her career, the Austrian-born Elizabeth Bergner.

The Prague audience's taste for energetic music and dance almost brought Josephine's tour to a premature close. After singing a couple of songs, Josephine embarked on her usual dance routine, accompanied by a full orchestra of local musicians.

Whether from enthusiasm or misunderstanding of their score, the musicians, under their conductor, suddenly began to quicken their tempo and Josephine was obliged to keep pace with the music. To her cries of 'Too quickly!' the conductor either ignored or misinterpreted her frantic signals to slow down and, encouraged by the growing excitement of the audience, he drove his musicians on in a frenzy of accelerating rhythm. The inevitable happened; Josephine slipped and fell, severely injuring her knee.

Furious with embarrassment, with blood streaming down her leg, Josephine resumed her dance, determined to outpace the demented orchestra. To the relentless rhythm they imposed, she took up the challenge and literally danced them to a standstill, and took an exhausted bow. Believing it all to be a part of the show, the audience went wild with delight, but back in her dressing room Josephine lay down at the point of collapse. The hazards of performing with unknown musicians, without adequate rehearsal, in a strange city, was a lesson she never forgot.

The tour was not without a tragic incident. In Budapest, on the last night of Josephine's appearances in a nightclub, a man shot himself. Nightly he had appeared alone at the same table, apparently absorbed in Josephine's performance. When the last customer had left he confronted Josephine and without a word put a pistol to his head. He was either mentally disturbed or an infatuated admirer, and the newspapers headlined the incident, 'Kills himself as she leaves... He couldn't live without the Black Venus!' The weekly Parisian theatrical magazine, *Les Coulisses*, led its weekly gossip column by revealing that 'a young Yugoslav singer, Mr Galor, killed himself in front of Josephine Baker, not for love of the Negress, but because he had no engagement to perform'. He was apparently an unemployed actor.

On the last night of her scheduled appearance at the Theater des Westens in Berlin, Josephine failed to appear at the theatre and there was evidence of a violent quarrel between her and Pepito. Perhaps the constraints of the current tour prevented her from again embarking on a reckless round of pleasure, as she had in Berlin three years earlier.

In the city of Pamplona in northern Spain, Josephine met more trouble. The city's Catholic Association protested against her appearance at the Olympia Theatre. Calling her a 'scandalous dancer' it published a circular inviting people to attend mass at the same time in the evening as Josephine's performance; the church of Saint Ignace was opposite the theatre. A fight broke out on the night, several people were injured, and the police made a number of arrests.

As Josephine made her way through Holland, Denmark, Sweden and Norway, her appearance before local dignitaries helped to overcome prejudice in some quarters and to restore her confidence. Her first appearance before royalty in a command performance before the King of Denmark bestowed upon her act the mark of respectability.

It was in Denmark that a feature of her future appearances was tried out. This was the quick change of clothes, in which she would surprise audiences by slipping out of sight for a few moments, to reappear a few seconds later in an entirely different outfit. During her Copenhagen performances, Josephine changed successively from the girdle of bananas to a loincloth of green feathers for her 'Ostrich' routine, then to shorts for her 'Shoeshine' act, and finally an evening gown for the finale when she sang a love song. Her command performance before the Danish monarch was the final accolade of her European tour before setting out for South America.

South America

In the spring of 1929, Josephine and Pepito sailed from Genoa on the *Conte-Verde* for a tour of South American states, including Argentina, Chile, Uruguay and Brazil. The voyage gave Josephine a respite from months of criss-crossing Europe by train and the endless changes of hotel and appearances in theatres and cabarets. As she settled into the luxurious first-class accommodation Pepito had booked for them, she recalled her earlier voyage from North America to Europe and the fears and apprehensions it had then held for her. This time she was famous, successful and ready to embrace a new continent.

As the *Conte-Verde* cruised off the coast of Brazil, Josephine observed the Sugar Loaf mountain with its statue of Christ rising above Rio de Janeiro. When the ship arrived late in Buenos Aires, crowds of people were anxiously awaiting the arrival, not of the *Conte-Verde*, but of 'The Josephine Baker'!

On board, three stewards guarded cabin No. 267 while the star slept. When Pepito, her manager, appeared he spoke in the 'aristocratic accents of a Count'! Then Josephine emerged dressed in a silver fox fur coat and hat and green shoes.

Her first encounter with the press set the tone of the Latin American tour. Intense interest focused more on her appearance and racial origins than her talents as a dancer. The *Critica* newspaper observed,

> Josephine's colour is indefinite, between terracotta and bronze… artificial colour conceals her real colour. If we touched her cheeks our fingers would show make-up. As for clothes, she is not

dressed as a black, no striking colours… Her manner is dignified but studied.

When Pepito was asked if Josephine would dance naked, he replied, 'No chance! Miss Baker is far from doing such a thing. In Paris, yes. It's the custom!'

Regarding his relationship with Josephine, Pepito was evasive. 'I am nothing, of no interest. We just came here to work. The rest is of no concern.'

'Do you belong to a noble family?'

'Please don't ask me anything. We just came here to work. No scandal about us!'

Josephine then came to the rescue. 'He's very modest. He never wants to talk about himself.'

Summing up Josephine's arrival, the *Critica* journalist wrote,

> We are all deceived. Josephine is not the shameless, acrobatic dancer we imagined, with contorted frenetic movements to jazz rhythms. She is a lady with poise. Her gestures are careful. If her smile appears graceful in a photo, it is even more so close to, and you can observe when she remains serious the lower lip reveals her racial origins… It's only beautiful from the whiteness of her teeth, also a characteristic of her race. Even though her father is Spanish she is an authentic 'negrita'. If her blood contains a mixture, the refinements come from European perfume and clothes.

More in admiration than condemnation the newspapers featured photos of the 'Scandalous Josephine' and the 'Femme Fatale'. While the paper with the largest circulation, *La Calle*, printed President Irigoyen's criticism of her, the opposition paper, *La Critica*, extolled her qualities. At the theatre Josephine's presence offered a pretext for demonstrations by opposing political parties.

From performing in Rosario and Cordoba in Argentina, Josephine moved to Uruguay to appear in Montevideo. There she renewed her acquaintance with Herman Von Keyserling, who had visited Chez Joséphine in Paris.

After Uruguay, Josephine went back on the road, or in this case railroad, crossing the continent by train, over the Andes mountains to Chile. As if to dramatise to the maximum her arrival, it took a message from President José Ibañez himself before frontier guards would let her make her way to Santiago.

In the Chilean capital the now familiar flurry of leaflets appeared on the streets with the words '¡*Atencion, Catolicos! He aquí la Baker!*' (Watch out, Catholics! Baker is here!). The President advised the Mayor of Santiago of the need for courtesy. Protests against her presence continued until President Ibañez visited the Astral Theatre, after which performances took place without incident.

After her debut, Josephine presented her producer, Charles Viban, with a nude portrait of herself, painted in oils by Jean-Gabriel Domergue, entitled 'The Black Venus'. In Valparaiso, Josephine caused a sensation when she danced the cueca, a kind of samba.

Travelling back across the southern part of the continent to Brazil, Josephine appeared in Sao Paulo before visiting Rio de Janeiro, which she called the 'City of Light of South America' – a reference to Paris's sobriquet. In first encounters between Josephine and her audience the 'current passed' and she was received 'like a long-lost sister'. Of a sightseeing tour offered by the city authorities, Josephine exclaimed later in Paris, 'Ah, what films one could make there! It's my dream to make a film in Rio de Janeiro, the capital of coloured people.' (The French director Marcel Camus did just that, with *Orfeu Negro* in 1959.) Josephine's interest in the cinema sprang from her recent unhappy experience with the medium in France where she had made her first full-length film, *La Sirène des Tropiques*.

In Rio harbour, the French ship *Lutetia* was steamed up ready to take Josephine back to France. On board she met Charles-Edouard Jeanneret, the Swiss-born French architect, who had been lecturing in Brazil. He told Josephine about the botanical gardens he had visited and confided that 'the city is made for man, not man for the city', a sentiment that many environmentalists would echo. But within five years, Le Corbusier, as he became known, was to build his first high-rise building in Rio, a fifteen-storey office block overshadowing the neighbouring nineteenth-century mansions.

Chapter Five

The Thirties: Cinema and Operetta

The Thirties for Josephine were years of intense activity in new and challenging areas of her personal and professional life. She would appear in two feature films, make numerous recordings of her songs and extend her talents to playing in light opera. She would return to America to perform in New York, and lose a loyal companion. Josephine would also marry and become a French citizen. Not all these events would bring satisfaction; some would bring distress in their wake. In the end it would be something over which she had absolutely no control that would offer her the greatest challenge, as the clouds of war began to gather over Europe. First, however, Josephine was invited to claim her place as a star of Grand Revue in Paris.

On their return to France from South America Pepito announced he had secured an engagement for Josephine to star at the Casino de Paris, the oldest and biggest music hall in the capital.

The thirty-year-old theatre in the Rue de Clichy had become the most prestigious traditional music hall in Paris. Since 1917, first under the direction of Leon Volterra, a former programme seller at the Olympia, and Jacques-Charles, who had helped to salvage the *Revue Nègre*, the Casino de Paris had presented the most celebrated names in popular entertainment. Gaby Deslys and Harry Pilcer had brought the first jazz band in Paris to play there, Maurice Chevalier and Mistinguett had created their legendary partnership on its stage, Yvonne Vallée, Fréhel, Marie Dubas, Raimu... all had helped to make the Casino de Paris the premier venue in France. That reputation was now in the hands of Henri Varna and Oscar Dufrenne, who invited Josephine to join that illustrious roll of performers.

The Casino de Paris 1930–32

Josephine had made her debut in Paris when the fervour of the 'Crazy Years' was at its height and her frenetic antics corresponded to the carefree, agitated mood of the Twenties. When she returned to France after her foreign tour, she again found herself, for new and different reasons, in the right place at the right time. On an astonishing tour of fifteen countries on two continents, she had appeared in some thirty cities, working in greatly varying conditions. Pepito had done his job well as tour manager and his protégée had become a fully-fledged revue artiste.

In the Twenties music hall had evolved from being a series of disconnected variety turns introduced by a master of ceremonies into revue, a series of tableaux linked together by a unifying theme, often built around the personality of a well-known leading artiste.

By 1930 the euphoria of *Les Années Folles* had worn off. The collapse of the New York Stock Exchange on Wall Street late in 1929 had worldwide repercussions and the economic realities of everyday life were reasserting themselves. Stringency and the widening economic depression had stimulated a demand for illusions of luxury and well-being. People wanted to forget hardship and unemployment and be entertained.

The cinema responded ideally to this desire to escape from reality. From being a mere novelty, films were already making inroads into traditional forms of entertainment. Theatres were being converted into 'talking picture halls' and specially built cinemas were making their appearance in city streets.

(The Moulin Rouge was one of the first Paris music halls to succumb to conversion into a cinema. Others, such as the Olympia, were to follow. When Griffith's *Birth of a Nation* was shown at the Drury Lane Theatre in London, the profits were so high and the running costs so low that it was feared that live entertainment could no longer compete economically with images projected on a screen. On European screens one could see Maurice Chevalier in his first Hollywood musical, *Parade d'Amour* or *Love Parade*, Marlene Dietrich in *The Blue Angel* and Jean Cocteau's *Le Sang d'un poète*).

But despite the undoubted attraction of black and white sound films the cinema still could not compete with the colour and movement of elaborately staged live musical theatre. By the Thirties this form of entertainment had developed into *Revue à Grand Spectacle*, or Grand Revue, featuring acknowledged star performers and a large supporting company in costly productions that sometimes ran for several consecutive seasons. Josephine's return to France coincided with the full flowering of Grand Revue in Paris.

Among the music halls vying for artists to top their bills in Grand Revue was the Casino de Paris. And of all the producers in the business, Henri Varna was the best qualified to give the public what it wanted. Taking over from Jacques-Charles, who had come from the Moulin Rouge, Varna and his associate, Oscar Dufrenne, had the authority and experience to see in Josephine the required star material. And of all the men who had managed the Casino de Paris, Varna was perhaps the most cultivated, despite the origin of his family name.

Small in stature with a round, sensitive face, Varna was born in Marseilles of a bourgeois provincial family whose real name was Vantard, meaning 'bragger' or 'boaster'. Varna's grandmother may have bragged about the quality of the fish she sold on the quayside of the Cannebière, but her grandson, Henri, was different. From a Jesuit upbringing Henri grew up to be a man of refined taste whose modest character concealed an inner strength of purpose. Abandoning his father's merchant business in Marseilles, he became an actor in the Belleville quarter of eastern Paris before joining forces with Oscar Dufrenne to write and produce revues. When he took over the Casino de Paris in 1924, Varna knew the business aspect of music hall from the inside.

Henri Varna defined his attitude to the music hall as 'an amusement for grown-up children'. And he insisted that its main quality was youthfulness. 'While a star should be experienced and in full possession of his or her talent, their main virtue is youthfulness. The music hall must recall the pleasant side of life and give us the desire to live! It is our duty to call upon great artists, painters, musicians of real talent. Only they can impress us immediately. Don't forget, we have to provoke laughter in a second, to excite us within a minute!'

In association with Dufrenne he had presented circus attractions and had astonished Parisians with such novelties as a corrida with real Spanish bulls, and a historic pageant at the Empire Theatre in which horses, elephants, crocodiles and lions had recreated an episode of *Quo Vadis*. The American rider, Tom Mix, had even galloped on horseback through the stalls... Varna's experience with animals, and audiences, had taught him how to deal patiently with temperamental humans and how to charm and surprise critical Parisian audiences.

There was another reason for Varna choosing someone of Josephine's qualities. Their next Grand Revue was timed to coincide with the Colonial Exhibition in Paris. As a celebrated coloured performer with African ancestry, Josephine's image would harmonise perfectly with a series of tableaux based on France's colonies.

At the Casino de Paris Varna marshalled his forces with gentle but firm persuasiveness. In his experienced hands Josephine acquired a certain poise and she listened respectfully to his advice from the moment rehearsals began.

Not everyone had the same confidence in Josephine's ability to carry off the role demanded of her. Earl Leslie, the American choreographer, doubted that Josephine could make a dignified entrance down the steep staircase as gracefully as Mistinguett had done only months before. (The fifty-seven-year-old star had agreed to loan 'her' Earl Leslie to Varna, and she watched rehearsals with more than casual interest.) Oscar Dufrenne, directing the music and songs, was fearful of what the public would think of Josephine's singing voice. But Varna's will prevailed. He coached and encouraged her as he had Mistinguett the previous year for *Paris-Miss*. Slowly he instilled in Josephine the necessary confidence and self-assurance to become the next star of the Casino de Paris.

Varna's rehearsals lasted into the early hours of the morning, as he studied minutely every detail of settings, staging, dance movements and songs. As rehearsals proceeded Josephine was pleased to see Paul Colin coming and going as he planned and painted decor for *Paris qui Remue*, (*Bustling Paris*), the chosen title of the new revue. Colin was sharing the design work with five other decorators. Josephine and Colin were pursuing parallel courses that had begun five years earlier with the *Revue Nègre* at the Théâtre des Champs-Élysées.

Vincent Scotto

It was at this moment that an energetic little man, also from Marseilles, entered Josephine's professional life. Vincent Scotto was a composer of music hall songs with a seemingly inexhaustible fund of tunes. Born in 1875, he arrived in Paris in 1906, the year of Josephine's birth, with the firm intention of bringing to the capital the melodies he had begun to create in the Midi.

Scotto viewed Paris as a provincial or a foreigner viewed it, to be courted and seduced, and he applied his talent to writing and selling his songs. Despite a musical education he could not play the piano but composed on a guitar which rarely left his side.

Such was his perseverance that it did not take Scotto long to find buyers for his songs. Music hall artistes and their managers had a voracious appetite for new material. Soon they were all making their way to his one-room lodging in the populous Saint Martin quarter to buy songs or commission new ones. From his tiny office Scotto dispensed new songs like betting slips – some were winners and some also-rans.

One day Scotto received a message from Henri Varna at the Casino de Paris announcing that he had engaged Josephine Baker and requesting a song specially for her. It was the kind of demand Scotto had received scores, if not hundreds, of times and usually he had no difficulty in fulfilling the request within days, even hours. But on the appointed day when he was to see Varna at the theatre Scotto had still not found an idea suited to Josephine's personality.

Walking to his appointment with his friend and collaborator, Leo Koger, Scotto still had not a single new idea in his head. Suddenly he stopped in a doorway; what if Josephine were to sing about her country and Paris? Without hesitation he scribbled down the first few notes of a melody which the idea suggested. Koger added a few words on the same theme, and they pressed on to their meeting. When they arrived at the theatre, Varna, Dufrenne and Josephine were waiting anxiously. Varna invited Scotto to climb on to the stage and sing his song, while Josephine listened from the stalls.

'*J'ai Deux Amours, Mon Pays et Paris*,' sang Scotto to the empty auditorium.

It took them only a few moments to decide that with suitable orchestration and presentation the new song would suit Josephine perfectly. Despite initial doubts about Josephine's voice, expressed by Oscar Dufrenne, Varna's collaborator, the song was completed as a slow foxtrot, and entitled *J'ai Deux Amours* ('Two Loves Have I' in the English version).

To advertise *Paris qui Remue* and adorn the cover of the programme, Varna had commissioned a talented young artist called Zig. '*Petit Zig*', as he was affectionately known, had designed for Mistinguett and he produced an image of Josephine very different from the brash 'hoofer' with the hitched-up skirt that Paul Colin had drawn for the poster for the *Revue Nègre*. Zig depicted a slim, chaste Josephine standing in a modest pose, emerging from a mass of light feathers, adorned in bangles and beads. Beside her, in the same decorative style, she was being offered a bouquet of flowers in a begging attitude from her newest partner, Chiquita, the pet leopard which Varna had bought for her as a publicity ploy. Zig's design set the tone for the new image of Josephine's elegance and style that accorded with Varna's conception of his revues. As he told the press, 'I want to make revues like picture books, pleasant in themselves, without necessarily being linked to topicality and repeatedly wanting to arouse the baser instincts; I want to offer snatches of daydreams…'

Josephine Versus Dolly

As Josephine's celebrity and self-assurance increased, so too did her vulnerability to bouts of petty jealousies. One incident during the rehearsals for *Paris qui Remue* illustrates her emotional sensitivity.

As an insurance against Josephine's possible illness, Henri Varna had engaged an understudy who could step in at a moment's notice if Josephine was unable to appear. The stand-in, Dolly Dihouri, was a lookalike who possessed Josephine's physique and colour and had learned all the dances and songs in the role. These included the celebrated show-stopper, *J'ai Deux Amours*, which Josephine sang with her partner, Pierre Meyer.

During one sketch in the revue Josephine and Meyer embrace and appear to kiss. When Dolly Dihouri rehearsed the scene with Meyer, Josephine found their embrace too realistic. She demanded that Varna sack not only her understudy, but Meyer as well! As a pretext she claimed that Dolly Dihouri did not sufficiently resemble her if required to take over the role.

To keep their star happy, Varna and Dufrenne agreed to release the understudy. Miss Dihouri, who claimed to be the Countess Capelet de Bourgouin, immediately sued for breach of contract. Through her lawyer, she offered to appear in court wearing a banana costume for the court to judge if indeed she could take Josephine's place.

The court declined her offer of a demonstration, but ruled in her favour. Varna and Dufrenne were ordered to pay Dolly Dihouri 14,000 francs compensation for insufficient notice of dismissal. And the actress was given the benefit of the doubt over her ability – or lack of it – to understudy Josephine. Honour was appeased, at a price.

Paris qui Remue

Paris qui Remue, or *Bustling Paris*, opened on 26 September 1930. Produced by Henri Varna and Earl Leslie, it contained a series of forty-five elaborate scenes giving full range to Varna's invention and Josephine's talents. It brought together the choreography of Earl Leslie and the stage design of Paul Colin; Oscar Dufrenne directed the vocals and the songs were composed by Vincent Scotto. Varna had assembled a galaxy of supporting artists, including French cancan dancers, a Russian ballet, Pills and Tabet and the 'Original 16 Jackson Girls and Boys'. There was even Joe Alex, who had shared Josephine's leap to fame in the *Revue Nègre*. A Brazilian jazz group entertained patrons in the entrance hall of the theatre.

That stalwart correspondent of the *New Yorker* magazine, Janet

Flanner, was there to report that 'Josephine Baker's new Casino show contains something of everything, including Pierre Meyer, and practically no feathers and furs'.

It did have wings, however. The first scene in which Josephine appeared was entitled '*L'Oiseau des Forêts*' and as an exotic 'Bird of the Forests' she wore a pair of huge white wings and performed a hopping, flapping dance to escape two hunters trying to capture this strange creature. The scene was such a success that Josephine quickly forgot that she had at first refused to wear the huge white wings.

Janet Flanner breathlessly summarises the main ingredients of the revue which had

> ...excellent imported British dancing choruses of both sexes, a complete Russian ballet, trained pigeons, a live cheetah, roller-skaters, the prettiest Venetian set of the century, a marvellous first-act finale, acres of fine costumes, the four best cancan dancers in captivity, a thriller in which Miss Baker is rescued from a typhoon by a gorilla, and an aerial ballet of heavy Italian ladies caroming about on wires.

Jacques Pills and Georges Tabet made a major breakthrough when they sang in harmony, *Couchés dans le Foin* ('Sleeping in the Hay'). With Tabet at the piano the duettists had injected jazz rhythms into traditional-type French ballads. The critics said it was like 'a breath of fresh air!'

One could add that Paul Colin's scenic designs were greatly admired and featured heraldic compositions of the radiators of the foremost makes of motor car... Voisin, Bugatti, Delage, Rolls-Royce and Chrysler, in a scene entitled 'The Nobility of the Automobile'. *Bustling Paris* got off to a busy start with a tableau of street vendors criss-crossing the stage crying the merits of French newspapers... *Le Matin, le Petit Parisien, l'Intransigeant* and *l'Humanité*... Grand Revue was living up to its name!

Despite the proliferation of talent in such a kaleidoscope of scenes, it was Josephine whom most people came to see and it was she who held the revue together. As one critic put it, the Casino de Paris was 'full of cannibals ready to devour Josephine on the opening night'. Josephine was approaching the summit of her pre-war celebrity and her emergence as a fully fledged revue artiste coincided with the full flowering of Grand Revue in France. At twenty-four she had the necessary youthfulness and energy to head a cast and display her experience. The audience was not disappointed.

The *New York Times* summed up her rapid rise to stardom thus:

> There was a time when Miss Baker's appeal to the Parisian was due in the main to her exoticism. She has a figure that looks best when she has little on. And she can wear little with a naturelness of a lithe and splendid animal. There was in her singing and dancing also something of the untamed animal that touched the heart of the ultra-civilised Parisian. Then she toured the world for two-and-a-half years. And what a change... She has mastered French. She also speaks Spanish and Italian. To see her doing dramatic parts, doing them not merely with skill but with a power and sensibility which holds the audience spellbound, is to wonder whether it is the same Josephine who showed Parisians how to dance the Black Bottom.

The German novelist, Erich Maria Remarque, who had just published his war novel, *All Quiet on the Western Front*, saw Josephine as bringing 'a breath of jungle air and the force of elemental beauty onto the stages of western civilisation...'

The *New Yorker* dug deeper into the phenomenon.

> ...she has, alas, almost become a little lady. Her caramel-coloured body, which overnight became a legend in Europe, is still magnificent, but it has become thinned, trained, almost civilised... On that lovely animal visage lies now a sad look, not of captivity, but of dawning intelligence.

Josephine's extended range did not impress the critic of the *Revue de Paris*, who, in the December issue, wrote,

> ...Alas, the brown goddess is no longer content to dance and amuse the public with childish monkey faces. She sings. She acts. She models designer clothes... For our part we admire her young body whose intuitions are often so right, but rather than having a

> Negress in evening dress we might as well have any white fashion
> model from the Rue de la Paix.

It took a provincial French newspaper published in Nice to reveal a whiff of backstage discrimination when it wrote that the dancer, Harry Pilcer, had refused Henri Varna's offer for him to appear in *Paris qui Remue* because of Josephine's presence. The paper wrote,

> Pilcer, who is American and an Anglican, is said to have an insurmountable dislike of Negroes, and already made a scandal at the Moulin Rouge when a black performer called Higgins was engaged in the same revue as Pilcer. Pilcer left to dance in the *Nudist Bar* at the Palace Theatre, but failed to make a hit there.

The journalist added his own comment when he ended his column saying, 'One cannot help smiling at such sensitivity when one remembers that Harry Pilcer is of dual Semitic and Austro-Hungarian origin.'

The first half of *Paris qui Remue* ended with a tableau celebrating the French colonies. The scene evoked the French Colonial Exhibition being held in Paris, which extolled the people and products of Martinique, Algeria, Madagascar and Indo-China... Joe Alex, Josephine's partner from *Revue Nègre* days, played the part of a sugar planter, surrounded by a full company in traditional costumes. Josephine then arrived to sing *La Canne-Sucre* ('Sugar cane') and stepped down from the stage to offer sticks of barley sugar, specially supplied by the firm Marquise de Sévigné, to spectators in the stalls. The Paris authorities elected Josephine 'Queen of the Colonial Exhibition', and she was photographed at the exhibition hall in front of an obscure wind instrument from Equatorial Africa.

In the hothouse atmosphere backstage at the Casino de Paris a tragi-comedy of infatuation was played out when Josephine fell in love with Tabet's partner, Jacques Pills. It began when Pills temporarily replaced the actor Ralph Erwin in all the scenes in which Josephine acted. As their relationship developed offstage, Josephine left her Le Vésinet home for the Pills household, leaving Pepito jealous and humiliated. The affair did not last long. Sensing problems ahead for the huge enterprise that literally revolved round Josephine, Varna cancelled Pills's and Tabet's contract, and their names disappeared from the second edition of the programme. Their two roles were taken over by Jean Irace and Jacques Erwin and the show continued.

The second half of *Paris qui Remue* was marked by four new songs by Vincent Scotto, sung by Josephine. The first, *La Petite Tonkinoise* tells the story of a 'little girl of Tonkin', a province of the former French protectorate of Indo-China, now Vietnam. This was followed by *Ounawa*, then *Dis-nous, Josephine* ('Tell us, Josephine') and finally the trademark *J'ai Deux Amours*. It was Josephine's rendering of the last that made the biggest hit.

J'ai Deux Amours was a departure from the usual type of song sung by Josephine in that it appeared to reflect her own story of an exile recalling her homeland in her country of adoption. The song also brought tears to the eyes of French provincials who regarded themselves as exiles in the capital. It was an immediate success and would have been difficult for another artiste to sing it with true meaning. The charm of Josephine's rendering, in her curiously accented French, gave it a distinction that could not be imitated and it became 'her song' and signature tune in the years ahead.

Writing in the theatrical weekly *Le Ramp*, Legrand-Chabrier said,

> Josephine personifies the music hall, possessing its essentials. Bouncing in a thousand and one movements, transfused by the music, she is a grimacing urchin, a stylish European, a sentimentalist... her tall slender body seems always dislocated, her teeth in the wind, warm cooing in the throat.

The last scene of the show – now entitled *La Joie de Paris* – was called 'A Water Fairyland', and featured a real cascade of 400,000 litres of water poured on the stage from hidden tanks, thanks to the skill of two aquatic engineers borrowed from the Colonial Exhibition.

Reviews of Josephine's Recordings

Reviewing new gramophone records in the Paris *Radio Magazine* in December 1930, Dominique Sordet suggested that

'Mademoiselle Joséphine Baker is a tempting quarry for record publishers'. Under the headline 'Joséphine Has a Voice', he wrote, 'The vocal talents of the young black star are shown here in a different way than from under the spotlights.'

Of Josephine's first recording of *La Petite Tonkinoise* (issued by Columbia – DF 229), Sordet notes,

> Joséphine Baker's voice is strongly Americanised, above all in this harsh, metallic medium. The high notes, clear and light, have great attraction. The rises and falls of the voice are pleasant, the delivery easy, the intonation correct.

But the critic then remarked that 'the accent is dreadful. One hardly understands *La Petite Tonkinoise* although it's delightfully warbled...' Sordet then offered readers a phonetic interpretation of Josephine's rendering:

> Je souis viv', je souis chamante
> Com' un p'tit ouaseau qui tchante...

Josephine's next release on the Columbia label fared better with Sordet. In *Suppose* (DF 230), Joséphine Baker rivals 'Sophie Tucker or Vaughn de Leath in touching charm,' he wrote, adding, 'one will note the irresistible saxophone which amorously intertwines with the singer's voice at the right places.' Finally Sordet advises those who know no English to ignore the words, which, he says, are probably without interest, and to 'abandon oneself unreservedly to the almost animal, physical grace of this charming voice'.

Josephine and Mussolini

In 1932, *Paris qui Remue*, which had run for thirteen months, was updated to become *La Joie de Paris*. In the pause between the two editions of the revue, Josephine made a brief visit to Italy to perform at the Teatro Lirico in Milan and to visit Rome.

The crisis between Italy and Abyssinia was at its height, and Italian troops were preparing to invade the country now known as Ethiopia. Benito Mussolini had declared that Abyssinia was Italian, and Josephine heard him deliver a belligerent speech justifying his intentions. She was told he wanted to put an end to slavery in that East African country. She was so overcome with admiration at this that she asked to meet the dictator face to face.

For all her political naivety Josephine was not alone in her opinion of Il Duce. Many learned conservative societies as well as some members of the French Academy were to sign a petition approving Italy's military intentions. (Vincent Scotto had even written a marching song entitled *Viva Musso* to words by Lucien Boyer, published by Salabert in the 1920s.)

Josephine returned to Paris and made some imprudent remarks about her Rome visit which were immediately given wide publicity. She had not yet learned that her celebrity and occasional access to prominent personalities called for discretion when making public statements. Josephine's visit to Italy was to have unforeseen consequences when war divided Europe a few years later.

La Joie de Paris

For *La Joie de Paris* Varna and Leslie presented fresh attractions and new personalities joined the cast, notably the Argentine-born guitarist, Oscar Aleman, who now led Josephine's orchestra.

A new programme printed in three languages (English, French and German) gave details of the fifty different scenes contained in the two acts of the revue. A huge 10,000-kilo revolving stage brought successive historical and modern settings into view, with evocative titles such as 'The Wonderful Palette of Paul Colin', 'Man and the Machine', 'The Sun Woman' and 'The Enchanted Village'…

Josephine appeared in a series of costume changes that drew instant applause. Against a backcloth inspired by the Monkey House at Chantilly, she descended, not from a tree, but down the redoubtable golden staircase, mastered by Sorel and Mistinguett. And in the scene entitled 'The Song of Jazz' she was accompanied by Oscar Aleman and twenty-two coloured musicians in a rousing intermission set.

Critics approved the pace and variety of mood and observed how co-designers, Paul Colin and Jean Le Seyeux, had excelled themselves in creating a series of dazzling tableaux.

As the two long seasons of *Paris qui Remue* and *La Joie de Paris* came to an end, Henri Varna and his associate, Oscar Dufrenne, must have known that they had written a unique page in French music hall history. Never had so many talented performers in the art of Grand Revue, combined to present such a galaxy of colour, movement and song. Against scenic effects that varied every few minutes, audiences were captivated by the unfolding album of Varna's cherished 'daydreams'.

Other forms of entertainment would claim larger audiences, use up talent quicker, lower standards, but only an evening spent in the electric atmosphere of the crowded auditorium of the Casino de Paris would remain in the collective family memory. And when the crowd poured out of the theatre into the Rue de Clichy, the song that rang in their heads as they made their way home was the simple, unforgettable melody of *J'ai Deux Amours*, sung in Josephine's inimitable manner. If she never sang another song, the first ten notes would forever remind people of her love for her country and for Paris. It was already 'her' song and would echo down the years as a cry from the heart from a black girl who found fame and fortune in the City of Light.

An English journalist caught the atmosphere of this venerable Paris theatre, when he wrote years later,

> To enter the darkened foyer of the Casino de Paris on a grey autumn day is to feel the weight of years among the mirrored columns and musty red and gilt decoration. Small showcases like shrines contain black and white photographs of Henri Varna, Mistinguett, Maurice Chevalier and Josephine Baker. How young they look! Listen! On the other side of those heavy padded doors the ghosts of thousands of past audiences are murmuring, the echoes of legions who found themselves united with the artistes on stage in a hundred different revues... You can hear them still, but don't open the doors. You may frighten away the ghosts of those past triumphs.

European Tour

When *La Joie de Paris* closed in 1933, after 346 performances, Josephine went on tour, beginning with her London debut at the Prince Edward Theatre. She took with her her jazz ensemble led by Oscar Aleman, sixteen 'Baker Boys' from the jazz group, and danced with her partner, Spadolini. The show ended with Josephine and the full company in 'The Story of Jazz'. The tour took them to Holland, Belgium, Greece, Turkey, Finland and Egypt. Back in Paris, Josephine was immediately taken up with the making of the film *ZouZou*, also starring the French actor, Jean Gabin.

It was during her appearance in Belgium that Josephine first met the man who was destined to become a professional and business associate and ultimately her last husband. Joseph Bouillon was a band leader playing at the Ostend Casino where Josephine was billed to appear in the floorshow. He was a prize-winning violinist from a family of musicians who had formed his own jazz group. He was so impressed with Josephine's performance that he asked for her signed photograph. She duly wrote on it, *To Jo Bouleon* (sic). He kept the misspelt dedication as a souvenir.

Cinema and Operetta

ZouZou

It was at this period that Josephine made her second foray into films. *ZouZou* traces the story of a Creole laundress of Marseilles who dreams of her native island beyond France, and also of becoming a celebrity in Paris, while running a hot iron over other people's washing. *ZouZou* was written by G Abatino, Pepito's cousin; dialogue was by Carlo Rim and Albert Willemetz, and the film was directed by Marc Allégret, André Gide's nephew.

Although the story of *ZouZou* had an all-too-familiar ring to it, and Josephine would simply once again be playing herself, it was a serious production which offered her the opportunity of appearing with experienced actors under the direction of professional film makers. Above all she played opposite a veteran performer of her own age at the start of his own film career, Jean Gabin.

ZouZou contained a number of songs, sung by Josephine and Gabin. Gabin sang *Viens Fifine*, a Java specially composed by Vincent Scotto; Josephine sang the languid *Haiti*, also by Scotto, and the seductive *C'est lui* (Why is there only one man in Paris...?) by Georges Van Parys, complete with Josephine's version of a 'growl trumpet'.

The film crew found Josephine amenable and tireless, anxious to please the director. Josephine was impressed by Jean Gabin's tight-lipped manner which was to become his trademark, and could not decide whether he was acting or not. 'Just behave as you are,' Gabin advised Josephine, 'I don't see why you should be afraid.'

In the story, ZouZou, played by Josephine, adopts a little dog – 'Biquet' (loaned by Joe Alex) – and a tiny caged bird. As the bird is symbolically set free, Josephine gains her freedom from the laundry to become a music hall artiste in Paris. But she is the loser in her love affair, not with Gabin, who plays a friendly matelot, but with her 'Julot', played by Teddy Michaud. When Josephine asked Pepito why the film had not ended with her marrying Gabin, Pepito replied ambiguously, 'ZouZou belongs to her profession as a star, as you do...'

It was not a reply that satisfied Josephine, who once said she would have married Pepito if he had agreed to her having a child.

Josephine was instrumental in launching a younger French actress on her long career in the cinema, when Viviane Romance was found a small role in *ZouZou*. The film had the benefit of wide publicity. Six hundred thousand copies of a news-sheet entitled 'Journal of ZouZou' were distributed to advertise the film's release in 1935. The communist newspaper *l'Humanité* wrote of '*ZouZou*' that it was 'the only film about the music hall made in France that can compete with American productions'.

La Créole

Josephine's performance in *ZouZou* encouraged Albert Willemetz, who had written the dialogue for the film, to extend her talents towards the legitimate theatre. As a prolific songwriter for Mistinguett and Chevalier, Willemetz proposed casting Josephine in the role of Dora in Jacques Offenbach's light opera, *La Créole*.

Among the ninety or so light operas Offenbach had written, *La Créole* had not been performed since 1876, when Anna Judic had played the title role. Anna Judic had been a versatile nineteenth-century artiste who had moved with ease from music hall to opera. Physically and in temperament, Josephine was right for the part but her voice needed training to sustain Offenbach's light, melodic score. While Willemetz and Georges Delange set about adapting the music and lyrics to Josephine's particular talents, Josephine agreed to take singing lessons from Madame Paravicini, who had coached the actress Yvonne Printemps.

The story of *La Créole* is like a fairy tale, full of intrigue and fantasy in an exotic setting. Dora is a beautiful Creole from Jamaica, loved by René, but his uncle wants him to marry Antoinette, who in turn prefers Frontignac to René.

When Josephine took to the boards at the Paris Marigny Theatre in *La Créole*, comments were generally measured and generous. Notices ranged from '...she sings, dances and acts exquisitely...' to '...her varied, personal and lively acting carried the entire troupe and delights the audience. She acts with moving sincerity, sings exquisitely, and dances with all her old abandon and grace.'

The fashionable London *Tatler* magazine noted that Josephine's voice 'is "husky" in the middle range and soars to a boyish treble...' The anonymous reviewer, who was among the specially invited guests at the *répétition générale*, observed how the

> blasé audience loved her delighted, almost bashful gratitude for the reception she received, and the unaffected way in which she carried on with every scene, instead of taking encores that the orchestra leader, Monsieur Labis, and the spectators, accustomed to the eager acquiescence of more sophisticated stars, obviously expected of her.

The continental edition of the London *Daily Mail* wrote of her 'brilliant promise in operetta' and suggested that librettists and composers should provide a repertoire necessary to display her 'physical and temperamental individuality', a way of reminding readers that this was Josephine, the frenetic jazz dancer of the Twenties, bringing new vitality to an operetta written half a century earlier.

Janet Flanner, of the *New Yorker* magazine, put the event into historic perspective when she wrote in her column,

La Créole is not Offenbach's best work, but it is Miss Baker's up to date, and might have been written for her, so appropriate are the light, innocent melodies… to her high, airy voice, half child's, half thrush's.

The French columnist, Régis Gignoux, viewing the Thirties in France, wrote in *Les Annales* of

…the influence of nudism, the return to nature, the mania for athletic sports… One will also see numerous artistes leave for America. Make way for youth! The question of Miss Josephine Baker's nomination for the Comédie Française will be raised…

One critic simply said that *La Créole* for Josephine was the 'turning point in her life'. Perhaps, but what seemed certain was that Josephine acquitted herself in a new and difficult role and her charm and youthfulness more than compensated for her inexperience in an art of whose traditions she was totally unaware. Josephine was to revive *La Créole* twice in the following years in unusual circumstances… But there was no sequel to Josephine's incursion into comic opera, except for a brief recital at the Cannes Casino, at the invitation of Renaldo Hahn, a Venezuelan composer and performer of Offenbach's music.

A Second Sound Film

Hard on the heels of *ZouZou* came Josephine's second feature film, *Princesse Tam-Tam*, directed by Edmond T Gréville, with the up-and-coming male lead, Albert Préjean.

Filmed partly on location in Tunisia, Josephine plays Aouina, a poor young Bedouin caught stealing fruit in a market. A young French writer, estranged from his wife who is having an affair with a maharajah, conceives the idea of bringing Aouina to Paris to pass her off as a princess in revenge. He is so successful that Josephine falls in love with him, and his wife hastily returns to her husband.

Once again it was a story based on Josephine's personality and character. And once again the scenario denies Josephine the man she wants. She is not even given the maharajah as compensation! To remind cinema viewers who is the star of the film, Josephine does get to perform some spectacular dances. The French cinema had still not dealt with racial differences as a reality, and *ZouZou* reflected the stereotypes current in Hollywood films.

Arrival and Departure

With her appearances at the Casino de Paris, Paris adopted Josephine once and for all, and her two seasons at the Rue de Clichy became the consecration of her status as an establishment figure of French music hall hitherto dominated by Mistinguett. Just as the Folies Bergère had given Josephine her celebrated banana costume, so the Casino de Paris had produced the theme song with which she would be associated for the remainder of her life. More than that, her foreign tours had broadened her appeal and proved her stamina. Her youthfulness, talent and experience had enabled her to reach a watershed in her career. Henri Varna had enabled the mature artiste to emerge. She had the world at her feet.

Josephine's name, her presence on the stage and cinema screen and her singing voice on records, all became part of French life of the Thirties. Even her particular pronunciation of the language, so dear to the French for whom accent betrayed origin and social standing, became familiar and reassuring. She joined the hierarchy of *vedettes* constantly quoted in the popular press, heard on the radio, and talked about in the cafés.

Journalists wrote her up routinely, no longer concerned with her age or origins, safe in the belief that 'true' facts were less important than keeping alive the legend. It was at this moment when she was on the crest of a wave of adulation that Josephine felt ready to make the journey all exiles feel impelled to make at least once in their lives – back to her country of origin. Would her proclaimed love of Paris, of which she sang so ardently, be returned by those of her homeland? There was only one way to find out.

During the run of *La Créole*, the American comedian, Eddie Cantor, paid Josephine a visit. As they talked in her dressing room Cantor related how Broadway revues were flourishing and suggested that Josephine make an appearance in New York. Although there were now fewer productions, creativity was sharpened, drama was more thoughtful and meaningful and musical comedy offered the public an escape from the hardship of the Depression years.

It was a vintage period of American musical comedy when some of the greatest popular song hits were created by such composers as Cole Porter, George Gershwin and Oscar Hammerstein II. Cantor talked of Ethel Waters and Beatrice Lillie, in their 'tour of the world in song' in *At Home Abroad*; of Cole Porter's songs, 'Just One of Those Things' and 'Begin the Beguine' in *Jubilee*; and Hammerstein and Romberg's work in *May Wine*. Most of all he enthused over Gershwin's monumental black opera, *Porgy and Bess*, which had just opened at the Alvin Theatre on 10 October 1935.

With her ten years' experience in Paris and on tour, with film and operetta credentials to her name, it seemed a propitious moment to return to the capital of American entertainment. Pepito immediately set about organising what was to be a daunting test of his managerial abilities. The result was a contract with Jake and Lee Schubert for Josephine to appear in the Ziegfeld Follies at the Winter Gardens Theatre in New York the following January, 1936. A subsequent tour of American cities would include Josephine's birthplace, St. Louis.

Ziegfeld Follies

Late in 1935, Josephine returned to the United States for the first time since she had left ten years before. Pepito had confirmed her engagement to appear in a Ziegfeld Follies revue in New York. On his return to Paris after making the final arrangements, he enthused over his impressions. 'It's a wonderful place, all new and friendly and hospitable,' he told Josephine. His optimism was not to be fulfilled; the visit proved to be a professional setback and marked the beginning of a series of personal misfortunes.

Josephine's delight in accepting an engagement with the famed Ziegfeld Follies was tinged with the regret that she would not appear under the personal direction of the founder, Florenz Ziegfeld, who had died three years earlier. She was to claim later that Ziegfeld had personally invited her for one of his earlier reviews when she had been under contract to the Folies Bergère in Paris.

For more than twenty years, Flo Ziegfeld had presented a series of lavish Broadway revues dedicated to the glorification of white American womanhood. He had created a category of performer called the 'showgirl', and had his own idiosyncratic system for auditioning his 'beauties'. He applied two implacable rules for testing aspiring applicants: the shoulder blades, the gluteus muscles of the back, and the muscles of the lower leg, must be in direct line with each other; and he never employed a girl with grey eyes, saying they were 'too intellectual and only belonged in college'. Ziegfeld's showgirls were noted for their superior unsmiling behaviour and inaccessibility offstage; but the daily milk bath he invented for Anna Held, one of his heading ladies whom he married, added to the legendary glamour of the Ziegfeld 'lovelies'.

The famed hauteur of the Ziegfeld showgirls, with their aloof, unsmiling gaze, dismayed Paul Derval of the Folies Bergère, who found them 'mass produced like a Chevrolet or a tin of ham'. Speaking of his own institution in Paris, Derval said, 'Our methods are entirely different. Greater stress is laid on the personality of each individual member of a troupe. I am a firm believer in the French maxim that uniformity breeds boredom. I select my dancers in the hope that each will claim the attention of a certain number of spectators.'

The collapse of the American stock market in 1929 had abruptly put an end to the extravagance of the revues at the Ziegfeld Follies. When Ziegfeld died three years later he left behind half a million dollars' worth of debts, but his second wife, the actress Billie Burke, attempted to keep the family tradition alive with revues bearing his name. In the midst of the Depression years, a Ziegfeld revue still offered audiences an illusion of luxury and opulence, and to be engaged as an attraction in a Ziegfeld show remained a mark of professional prestige.

It was with anticipation mixed with apprehension that Josephine and Pepito stepped ashore in New York in November 1935. Like every expatriate, Josephine yearned to be honoured in her own country. The need for a black American to do so was even stronger. The opportunity to perform in a Ziegfeld revue offered her the chance to prove that a non-white artiste could attain the same status on equal terms as a white artiste.

The American press was ready to welcome her:

> After ten years in the country to which she went as an anonymous chorus girl, Josephine is returning as an acknowledged performer to make the conquest of her own country. As Josephine says it, 'I must make the final conquest, I want to win the hearts of people at home.'

Another paper wrote:

> If Broadway expects to welcome back a Harlemised Josephine Baker this fall, it will have a sorry shock. The Josephine who is to appear in this winter's version of the Ziegfeld Follies is a far cry from the lively and naive stage debutante who arrived in France just ten years ago, October 2, 1925. Josephine will make even the most highbrow of Harlem take a back seat.

The Josephine who returned to New York aboard the luxury liner *Normandie*, with trunks of fine Paris clothes and a Ziegfeld contract, was very different indeed from the Harlem 'hoofer' who had timidly embarked for Europe ten years before. In the intervening period she had starred in revues at the Folies Bergère and the Casino de Paris, had sung in an Offenbach operetta, appeared in a sound film with Jean Gabin, and had toured European and South American cities as a heading artiste of the French music hall. With such an international reputation, it seemed to Josephine only natural that she should top the bill in the American capital of entertainment – New York. Nevertheless, it was not to be.

The visit was ill-omened from the start. The Ziegfeld management had failed to reserve accommodation for them at the classy Waldorf Astoria Hotel, as they had expected. When Josephine and Pepito arrived at the more modest St. Moritz Hotel facing Central Park, they were informed that, in conformity with the prevailing laws and customs, they would have to occupy separate rooms, because they were not married. The manager of the hotel then asked them not to use the main entrance lobby, because Southern guests were very sensitive about the colour issue and might complain about the presence of a black woman in the hotel. There was worse to follow.

When Josephine and Pepito paid their first visit to the rooftop Winter Gardens Theatre where the Ziegfeld revue was to be presented, they received another shock. They discovered that far from Josephine having star billing, as Pepito imagined he had secured, she was but one of a number of individually talented performers appearing under the Ziegfeld banner. The veteran artiste, Fanny Brice, was the star of the show and Josephine's name appeared third after a comedian named Bob Hope, who was also compère of the revue.

Josephine felt further humiliated when she was told that she would not be permitted to sing Ira Gershwin's song, 'What is There to Say?' which went to Fanny Brice, who was also to sing the English version of *Mon Homme* ('My Man'), the torch song originally made famous by Mistinguett at the Casino de Paris. Josephine was also overruled in the matter of the clothes she would wear in her three scheduled appearances. Against her better judgement she was persuaded to appear briefly in a version of her banana costume, to remind New York audiences of her celebrated dance at the Folies Bergère in Paris.

Josephine swallowed her pride and tried to find consolation in rehearsals. The fact that the Plantation Club, at which she had danced in the chorus line ten years before, lay at the foot of the Winter Gardens building of the Follies, was an uncomfortable reminder of her earlier difficulties with obstinate managements.

After a preliminary try-out at the Boston Opera House, the new edition of the Ziegfeld Follies opened in New York on Christmas Eve 1935. The ballet sequences were choreographed by George Balanchine, working for the Follies for the first time, and the stage designer was twenty-eight-year-old Vincent Minnelli. Ira Gershwin and Vernon Duke wrote the songs. The attractions included Judy Canova, Eve Arden, and the black dance duo, The Nicolas Brothers.

Josephine was featured in three song settings. In a scene representing the Longchamps racecourse in Paris, she sang *Maharmee*, veiled in a sumptuous sari. In a second tableau,

Josephine wore a closely fitting sheath of silver leaves that weighed seventeen pounds and sang *Cinq Heures du Matin* ('Five o'clock in the Morning'). Her third appearance was more in keeping with her popular image. She appeared in a Caribbean setting to sing 'Island in the West Indies', and then, dressed in her girdle of imitation bananas, she performed what was described as a conga.

The contrast between Josephine's outgoing, expansive style and the expressionless faces of the Ziegfeld girls could hardly have been greater. Josephine's flashing smile and uninhibited manner may have won some hearts, but the traditional, puritanical Ziegfeld atmosphere was all-pervasive.

When she sang *Cinq Heures du Matin* in French it irritated those for whom a song is a story sung in words they understand, however trivial the meaning or endearing the melody. 'If Billie Burke could sing "My Man" in English, why can't Josephine make the same transition?' people asked. Even when she sang in English, the critic of *The Nation* complained 'I didn't understand a word...' while the *New York Post* wrote of her 'curious dwarf-like voice eclipsed in the cavernous Winter Gardens'.

Ira Wolfert in *The American* described Josephine's voice as sounding like 'a cracked bell with a padded clapper' and added, 'still, I like it. I'm very fond of Chinese music.' The critics were no more charitable when it came to her dancing. 'Nudity and high-kicks are no longer the favourite theme,' wrote one journalist, while another confined his report to two flat sentences. 'Some like Josephine Baker. I don't like Josephine Baker.'

There was also an added irritant to Josephine's appearance. In his usual diligent manner, Pepito had organised a claque to lead the applause after each of Josephine's songs. Although this was not an unusual practice among some promoters (and would have been heartily approved of by Ziegfeld himself in his earlier days) Pepito was too heavy-handed for the élite Winter Gardens clientele. When they became aware that crude attempts were being made to manipulate them, they remained largely indifferent to Josephine's performances.

The critics immediately seized on misplaced efforts to influence their judgement. Leading the fold, the *Daily Mirror* wrote, 'Critics are not fooled by noise.' The report was signed by Walter Winchell, a journalist with whom Josephine was to cross swords in later years in a bitter legal battle over alleged racial discrimination in the exclusive New York Stork Club.

Rightly or wrongly, the blame for everything that had gone amiss since their arrival in New York fell on Pepito. Josephine angrily reproached him for not having negotiated a better contract protecting her star quality and billing. In addition, she blamed him for his inept handling of the claque and subsequent bad press notices.

With Josephine's loss of morale, their personal relationship rapidly deteriorated. Having coached Josephine for nearly ten years in the art of survival and social advancement, Pepito suddenly realised he was out of his depth. He had failed her in her own country and had lost his last hold over his protégée. The debacle in New York was his final defeat.

Perhaps jealousy over Josephine's casual liaisons rose up in his mind as being no longer tolerable. Alternatively, he may have learned of her secret visit to the man to whom she was still legally married in Philadelphia. (Despite a hasty separation from Willie Baker, Josephine was to keep his name professionally for the remainder of her life.) Whatever the reason for Pepito's sudden departure, a fatal illness was robbing him of the will to reaffirm his authority. He quickly packed his bags and left for Paris. Within weeks of his return to France, he was dead from advanced cancer of the kidneys.

Bereft of Pepito, Josephine pursued her course alone in New York. Following the practice he had initiated in the many cities in which she had appeared, Josephine adopted and re-baptised a cabaret, formerly called Mirage, on East 54th Street, Chez Joséphine. She immediately felt more at home being hostess each evening in an atmosphere of her own making after her Follies appearance. However, Pepito's defection and death affected her more deeply than she was willing to admit. She had lost her Pygmalion.

Josephine's first visit to her homeland in ten years was nearly over. In a live radio broadcast from New York, she spoke wistfully of Paris and in a tremulous voice, sang two songs, 'Time Was' in English, and *Le Chemin du Bonheur* (or 'Dream Ship') in French.

Before her return to France, Josephine suffered one more rebuff, from an unexpected quarter, when she was a dinner guest at a party given by the composer, Lorenz Hart, who was later to team up with Richard Rodgers. The guests were served by Hart's black maid, whose outspokenness was understood and tolerated by her employer. When the time came for coffee, Josephine turned to the maid and said, 'Donnez-moi une tasse de café, s'il vous plaît' – an unexceptional request in French for a cup of coffee.

The presence of another black women in the Hart household, as a guest to be waited upon, was too much for the servant. Quick as a flash she retorted, 'Honey, you is full of shit! Talk the way yo' mouth was born!'

Was it arrogance, or forgetfulness that she was in English-speaking company in America, that caused Josephine to address the maid in French?

Josephine left no documentary record of this period of her life. Adverse press notices of her Ziegfeld Follies appearance were studiously ignored and all references to Pepito were removed from her private papers. It was not until many years later that she talked to Stephen Papich, a tour manager on another American tour, and told him of the pain and disappointment of her first return to New York. Papich later recounted the episode in his book entitled *Remembering Josephine*. Papich offers many uncorroborated anecdotes of Josephine, allegedly related by the artiste.

It was to Stephen Papich that Josephine confided a curious story of an encounter with Billie Burke or Mrs Florenz Ziegfeld on board the liner *Normandie* that took Josephine to New York to appear in the Ziegfeld Follies. Josephine tells how she instructed the purser to convey an invitation to Mrs Ziegfeld to join her at her table for dinner.

Josephine was the first to arrive and made her entrance down a long stairway into the dining saloon to a standing ovation from everyone present, including the captain. When Billie Burke entered a few moments later, she was similarly applauded and led to Josephine's table where a chair was held out for her. Suddenly she brushed past the steward and marched out of the room amid stunned silence from the other diners. Josephine concludes the anecdote with the words, 'Billie Burke just glared at me for a moment. I knew then she was a nigger-hater!'

In the introduction to his book, Papich warns his readers that Josephine attributes certain incidents and events to different people at different times. 'Actually, many times the same incident did occur with several different people,' he reminds us.

The story of the *Normandie* incident as told by Josephine and dutifully recorded by Papich has all the hallmarks of an imagined encounter and all the vividness of a dream or nightmare. The long staircase and the applause, strangely reminiscent of Josephine's countless stage entrances; the captain standing with the assembled passengers, so very like an orchestra leader with an audience in the stalls.

For all its clarity, the brush with Billie Burke is uncorroborated by any other source and is almost certainly a fiction for the following reasons: Pepito, who accompanied Josephine on the voyage, would certainly have been at her side to conduct introductions and avoid embarrassing encounters which could head to snubs. Billie Burke was well known at that time as a Hollywood actress, yet she was far from being the dizzy blonde she played in films. If she had been on the same boat, it is unlikely she would have been unaware of the presence on board of Josephine, who was to appear in a revue bearing her family name.

All the pain and embarrassment of her first return to her country of birth, the disputes with the Ziegfeld management, the attacks from critics and the loss of Pepito, were combined by Josephine into the 'memory' of one hugely humiliating incident on board a luxury liner and played out in front of an audience of passengers. It was a device Josephine was subconsciously to use many times in her life to expiate the indignities she suffered as a result of her colour.

Return to the Folies Bergère

During the last weeks of Josephine's New York tour, she received an unexpected visit from Paul Derval, who was still pulling in the customers at the Folies Bergère with revues featuring statuesque nudes placed in historic period settings. Derval was experiencing competition from the Casino de Paris and wanted Josephine back. Unaware of her unhappy passage at the Ziegfeld Follies, Derval found Josephine the centre of attraction at her temporary cabaret appearances in New York. He invited her to star in his new revue at the Folies to coincide with the 'Great International Exhibition' in 1937.

After some firm but friendly haggling over her fee, a deal was struck. Derval returned to Paris with photos of Josephine in her Ziegfeld costumes and announced to the press, 'Straight from her resounding success in New York, Josephine Baker will be back within the month. She's as lovely and as vivacious as ever!'

Michel Gyamarthy designed the poster for *En Super-Folies*, which proclaimed 'Josephine is back at the Folies'. It depicted the star wearing only feathers and pearls but in a far less provocative pose than the one Paul Colin had created.

In October 1936, Josephine opened at the Folies Bergère in the new revue entitled *En Super-Folies*. After the slights endured in the Ziegfeld Follies, she was glad to be home again in the familiar atmosphere of the theatre she had not played in for ten years. As was her established custom, she opened another nightclub in her name, just off the Avenue des Champs-Élysées. It was an attempt to recreate the success of the original Chez Joséphine, when fashionable Paris had flocked to see her after her debut at the Folies. And since she was back again almost where it had all began, for a brief moment everything promised to be as it was before. The only shadow was the conspicuous absence of Pepito, the man who had been at her side for ten years.

Despite the rigorous rotation of titles composed around the word '*Folies*' the formula for *En Super-Folies* was little different from the preceding editions, except for the presence of Josephine. Scenes such as 'The Marvellous Jungle', 'White Magic', 'The Country Girl', 'The Most Beautiful Night of Don Juan', 'The Fountain of Love', and 'Madame Bovary' alternated every few minutes. Scenic designs were the work of a Hungarian artist, Michel Gyamarthy, who as a young costume and set designer in

Budapest in 1927 had created a poster for Josephine's first European tour. Gyamarthy brought a new dazzle and originality to tired versions of revue themes and eventually took over sole responsibility for the design and production at the Folies Bergère.

Josephine, for her part, brought a newly found Parisian chic and elegance to the theatre that had once extolled her brash exoticism. She appeared in one scene as Mary Queen of Scots; the tableau ended with a simulated execution in which a fake head was seen to roll while the orchestra reassuringly played *Ave Maria* before a cathedral decor of stained glass windows.

Josephine also brought French adaptations of two American songs to Paris. Cole Porter's 'Easy to Love' became *C'est Si Facile de Vous Aimer*, and 'There's a Small Hotel' by Rodgers and Hart was translated as *C'est un Petit Nid*. Both songs brought Parisians in touch with stage and screen successes currently showing in the United States. 'Easy to Love' came from the film *Born to Dance* and 'There's a Small Hotel' was sung in the musical comedy *On Your Toes*.

In the guise of a journalist, Colette attended a rehearsal and wrote appreciatively of Josephine's tasteful handling of her big nude scene entitled 'Tropical Passion' in which she is seized by three hunters. It was a rare note of professional understanding and the French authoress also wrote personally to Josephine saying, 'In exchange for the garden flowers you sent me, please accept my affectionate thoughts and heartfelt wishes. A kiss from your long-standing friend, Colette.'

A male nude dancer, Frédéric Rey, was noted by the critics. The Austrian-born dancer had been brought to Paris by Mistinguett and was making his first appearance in *En Super-Folies*. If Rey threatened to steal the show, Josephine received her due credit from the revue critic, André de Badet, who enthused,

> ...Amusing, sensual and sumptuous... the girls are beautiful enough to break down the resistance of Saint Antoine himself... the boys appear to have stepped down from metopes of a Parthenon... And above all there is Josephine Baker, more original than ever... Josephine, the little bird of the tropics, who sings without pause the songs of the sunny islands for the great,

grey city which adopted her one evening when she wasn't yet Josephine.

Among the crowds who applauded Josephine at the Folies Bergère in 1937, a young French soldier clapped louder than his neighbours from his seat in the balcony. Lucien Vierge, from a rural community in south-west France, was on his first visit to Paris. He was stunned by the sumptuousness of the revue and by Josephine's presence. Lucien would survive the coming war years and would return to his village to raise a family. He was destined to observe the real-life drama in which Josephine would once again be the principal player.

As French and foreign visitors flocked to the capital for the 'Great International Exhibition', many also found their way to Josephine's club in the Rue François Premier. Among them was Mark Connelly, the black author of the successful Broadway play, *The Green Pastures*. Another celebrity was the Austrian Franz Lehar; Josephine sang for the composer of the *Merry Widow* and *The Land of Smiles*, the song 'I'll Give My Heart...' For Josephine it all seemed like old times and, as a bonus, the dancer Frédéric Rey had become her close companion offstage. If it was but a passing affair, Rey was to reappear in different circumstances in the troubled years ahead and to remain a close friend. In the meantime, Josephine was looking for a more stable relationship.

Marriage and Misfortune

On 30 November 1937, the inhabitants of the commune of Crèvecoeur-Le-Grand, north of Paris, were alerted to a Parisian-style event in their small town hall. The mayor, Benjamin Schmidt, a prominent member of Parliament and former Undersecretary of State for Finance, conducted the marriage ceremony of his friend, a young French broker and aviator, Jean Lion, to Josephine Baker. Lion, the son of a wealthy Jewish industrialist, had known Josephine for several years and had courted her in recent months at riding stables in the Bois de Boulogne and when she obtained her pilot's licence. Rumours of a marriage had been consistently denied until the very last moment and the marriage was supposed to be secret. Witnesses to the civil ceremony were Paul Derval, director of the Folies Bergère, and Georges Lion, brother of the bridegroom.

After responding to the traditional questions put to the couple, Josephine was heard to giggle when Mayor Schmidt told Josephine that she must obey her husband and follow him everywhere he went. Josephine was then congratulated for becoming Madame Jean Lion and for having acquired French nationality through the marriage. The mayor said that since St. Louis, Missouri, Josephine's birthplace, was originally French, it was normal that she should 'return to the fold' one day. The marriage had the full blessing of Jean Lion's mother, Ernestine, and there was speculation that Josephine may have adopted the Jewish faith of her new husband.

As a crowd of well-wishers waited outside the town hall, local sportsmen fired their shotguns into the air and a gramophone played some of Josephine's latest songs. The newly married couple donated 10,000 francs to a local charity before departing with twenty guests for a wedding breakfast in nearby Beauvais.

Josephine made no secret of certain constraints in her relationship with Jean Lion. Only hours after the marriage she told journalists, jokingly, 'My husband and I quarrelled in the first minute we met. We've been quarrelling ever since. Very soon I suppose we shall have another row because he wants me to give up the stage.'

Jean Lion had been increasingly insistent that Josephine should retire, saying that a woman cannot be a wife and an actress at the same time. 'No more stage for Josephine after her London visit,' he declared firmly.

Josephine's appearances at the Folies had ended and she was due to appear in London within a week. She admitted she did not know what to do. 'It all turns on the question, Should a woman give in to her husband?' she said. But such was her affection for Jean that she compromised and allowed herself to begin a series of farewell tours, beginning in London. She could not simply disappear without the leave-taking that the public expected of her.

Jean accompanied Josephine whenever he could; combining business meetings with the satisfaction of seeing his wife announce her 'farewells' to the press and public. When he knew that she was pregnant, he forbade her to use her pilot's licence to fly a light aircraft. Josephine, for her part, prepared for the happy event.

In London, Tunis, Zurich, Warsaw and Nice it was the same exultation and sadness for Josephine, with blown kisses from the stage and the songs *J'ai Deux Amours* and 'Thanks For The Memory'. Her pregnancy gave Josephine the courage to say goodbye to the life she knew best and the music hall she loved. Even a tentative project for a role in a new musical comedy, proposed by Albert Willemetz, who had adapted *La Créole* for Josephine, could not deter her from the course she had chosen.

It was a simple enough event that changed everything. Following abdominal pains, a doctor was called. Josephine lost her unborn child. With that loss went the one thing that could have bound Josephine and Jean together. Despite her sadness, or because of it, the theatre reasserted itself. The tours resumed. Rome, Stockholm, Madrid, Berlin… At the divorce proceedings one year later the judge remarked that they were two individuals 'who never really knew each other…'

War Clouds Gather

From March 1939 Josephine toured South American cities, making a return call at Rio de Janeiro in July. Despite the warm welcome she received in the city she was eager to return to France to begin rehearsals for her new revue at the Casino de Paris. Its theme was to be 'Brazil', and in her luggage, besides the small menagerie of exotic pets she had acquired, Josephine had collected song and dance material to be incorporated in the new revue. She planned to introduce the samba and mocamba dances to the Parisian public, in homage to the country that had acclaimed her ten years earlier. But political events in Europe would dictate otherwise.

Within weeks of Josephine's return to Paris, France had joined Britain in declaring war on Germany, and general mobilisation was declared after the fall of Czechoslovakia and Poland. Following the fateful public announcement of 3 September, Henri Varna quickly abandoned the Brazilian project at the Casino and began to assemble a new revue entitled *Paris–London*, a theme more appropriate to the new Franco-British alliance. A British Expeditionary Force of 158,000 soldiers was already on its way to France to join French troops manning her eastern frontiers.

Josephine's close relationship with a young French industrialist had to be brutally cut short when Jean Meunier, a chocolate manufacturer, was enlisted in the French armed forces.

Josephine was to share top billing with Maurice Chevalier in *Paris–London*. Both performers were already known to British audiences and Josephine had appeared in London and Glasgow the previous year. (In Glasgow the Scottish authorities had banned Josephine's dance entitled 'Night in Algiers' for being too provocative. Henri Varna feared no such limits on Josephine's performance in wartime Paris!) Soldiers on leave in the French capital would welcome familiar faces to entertain them in a patriotic-sounding revue.

Both Maurice Chevalier and Josephine were experienced negotiators over the terms of their respective contracts. Billing is all-important to performers. The order of appearance on programmes and posters and the size of their names is closely studied by their agents to protect the standing of their clients in the eyes of the public.

Josephine rarely had to fight for top billing, and she was accustomed to get the fee she demanded. Chevalier had more trouble over billing than fee. (He had experienced this in Hollywood over his difference with Columbia Pictures, when he refused to accept second place in publicity for the projected film of Franz Lehar's operetta *The Merry Widow*, also starring Grace Moore of the Metropolitan Opera.)

Trouble immediately arose in *Paris–London* over the order of Josephine's and Chevalier's appearance. As both stars enjoyed equal status in the eyes of the public, the problem was, who should appear on the stage first, and even more importantly, who should close the second half of the revue?

Josephine's agent wanted the second half of the programme, customarily reserved for the strongest personality on the bill. Chevalier, for his part, refused to open the programme, generally given to lesser attractions. As the veteran of the two he claimed what he considered was his rightful place, the second half leading up to the finale. To everyone's surprise Josephine agreed without fuss to appear in the first half of the programme.

A try-out of *Paris–London* was staged for Allied troops manning the defensive Maginot Line in eastern France. Appearing before an exclusively male audience in uniform, Josephine was acclaimed by the soldiers who refused to let her leave the stage, demanding encore after encore before the scheduled interval.

This severely upset the timing of the revue since a night curfew had been imposed on front-line forces. While Chevalier sat fuming with annoyance in his dressing room, the second half of the programme he was to lead had to be radically curtailed. After Josephine's exuberant first half of the revue, the time left for Chevalier to sing became a hurried anticlimax.

Back in Paris, Chevalier offered Josephine the second half of the programme that he had earlier coveted. Josephine declined his offer and they both finally settled to occupy exactly the same time on the stage in their two separate halves. Honour was saved but the older artiste continued to nurse a grievance at being outmanoeuvred by the younger star.

Paris–London duly opened in wartime Paris and Josephine received an ovation for her rendering of Vincent Scotto's song, *Mon coeur est un oiseau des îles*. Maurice Chevalier re-established his pre-eminent position in the (full) second half of the bill and sang with patriotic fervour, *Ça fait d'excellents français*, and *Paris sera toujours Paris*. Civilian and military audiences alike responded to the patriotic, upbeat tone of the revue featuring two established top-line performers.

Chapter Six
Josephine's War

After the initial shock of France being at war with Germany for the third time within living memory, a defiant mood of 'business as usual' prevailed in Paris. Cafés, cinemas, theatres and nightclubs remained busy while the Allied governments pursued their appeasement policy with Hitler. France settled down to what came to be called the *drôle de guerre*, or phoney war, in which life appeared to go on as usual despite the build-up of military forces at the Franco-German frontier.

When France declared war on Germany, the French Intelligence and Counter-espionage Service found itself severely understaffed. While Germany had been steadily and methodically stepping up its information-gathering activities in France, lack of funds and government indifference had limited effective action by the Deuxième Bureau. As head of the German Section of French Intelligence, Alsatian-born Jacques Abtey began to seek additional help from voluntary informers. They were called *honorable correspondants* who were willing to offer their services for purely patriotic motives.

One of Abtey's *correspondants* was a theatrical impresario named Daniel Marouani, whose brother Felix happened to be Josephine's agent at that time. The Marouani brothers were members of a clan of Tunisian theatrical agents in Paris who represented such artistes as Maurice Chevalier, Tino Rossi and Edith Piaf. They knew Josephine well, having presented her on the Côte d'Azur. Daniel Marouani told Abtey, 'You should meet Josephine Baker. I am sure she can be of great service to you.'

Abtey was surprised at the suggestion. Since the First World War, the employment of women in intelligence gathering was considered highly risky. The memory of Mata Hari, the Dutch dancer, who had allegedly betrayed both sides in the conflict and had been executed in France, was still fresh in people's minds.

Marouani insisted, however, and took Abtey to meet Josephine at her mansion in Le Vésinet, west of Paris. She had been warned in advance of the encounter and expected to meet a typically dour French plain-clothes policeman in black bowler hat and raincoat. She was introduced instead to a young, clean-shaven, blond man, who could be mistaken for an American or Scandinavian. Over elegantly served refreshments Josephine told Abtey, 'It is France that made me what I am. I will always remember that. I am ready to give my life for her.'

Abtey was impressed by Josephine's calm assurance and declaration of loyalty to her adopted country, so different from the popular image of her extravagant stage personality. As a celebrity, her acquaintanceship with foreign diplomats could be turned to advantage. He decided to test Josephine's ability to move in official circles in Paris and gather fragments of information. Embassies remained foreign territory, but her friendly relations with the Italian Embassy, for example, might reveal that country's intentions in the war. She had previously expressed admiration for Mussolini's ambitions in North Africa.

Meanwhile, in Paris life appeared to go on as before but behind the facade of normality, apprehension and fear were taking over. By the spring of 1940, France's much vaunted defensive Maginot Line in the east had been bypassed. Hitler's armies had taken over Finland, Norway and Denmark and were moving towards Holland, Luxembourg and Belgium. In May, the Battle of Britain began.

As a mood of fatalism grew in Paris, people began to leave the capital. When receipts dwindled at the Casino de Paris, Varna closed the *Paris–London* show and shut the theatre. Josephine exchanged feathers and sequins for the white coat of a voluntary Red Cross worker and began caring for refugees flooding into France from the northern occupied countries. While listening to their tales of hardship, she learned of the pressures being exerted by the invading Nazi forces and of their persecution of blacks and Jews in the countries they had overrun.

After a day spent helping to comfort uprooted families traumatised by the turn of events, Josephine would return to the calm of Le Vésinet to reflect on the sudden changes brought about by the war. She would also relay what she had seen and heard at the refugee reception centres to her Intelligence 'controller', Captain Abtey.

Early in June 1940, uninvited by Hitler, Italy declared war on the Allies and joined the Axis powers. The Italian fascist leader, Benito Mussolini, seeing France on the verge of collapse, anticipated sharing in the spoils of a North African campaign.

The Fall of France

The fall of France was swift. As the German armies began their assault from the north, tens of thousands of Allied troops were evacuated to Britain through a bridgehead at the port of Dunkirk. Paris was bombed and the capital surrendered and was declared an open city. The government moved to Tours and then to Bordeaux on the Atlantic coast. Maréchal Pétain, who succeeded Prime Minister Paul Reynaud, sued for peace and the armistice was signed at Compiègne on 22 June 1940.

In Paris, the recently busy avenues and boulevards became empty of traffic; cafés and restaurants closed and the city became deserted except for German patrols. The vast Champs-Élysées Theatre and the larger hotels were requisitioned by the occupying forces. Many people abandoned their homes and businesses and fled to the country. Those who remained began timidly to emerge to view the enemy at close quarters. Shutters were raised and shops began to serve a new clientele dressed in the grey uniform of the German Wehrmacht.

Artistes in Wartime

Many artistes and intellectuals faced the dilemma of how to contribute effectively to a common cause in wartime, according to one's ability and conscience. Graphic artists have depicted the horrors of armed conflict; poets in uniform have recorded the anguish of separation and death; writers have glorified valour and bravery under fire. Entertainers have often felt that the best way to serve their country is to continue to exercise their profession, either in or out of uniform.

Some entertainers in France continued to appear before French and German occupying forces alike, rather than refuse their artistic activities. The French cinema remained active in the closed environment of the sound studios. (Josephine had a singing role in *Fausse Alerte* being directed by Baroncelli in 1940.) Maurice Chevalier and Mistinguett were among numerous performers who played before mixed audiences in theatres that remained open or broadcast from Radio Paris.

Chevalier justified his decision by saying, 'An entertainer's profession is his whole life. If we have to fight for France, or die for her, we are ready to do so. But the rest of the time we just want to be left alone. I guess we feel we are doing our share by giving laughter and gaiety to the nation.'

One popular comedian in a nightclub took the risk of coming on stage with one arm outstretched giving the Nazi 'Heil Hitler!' salute. Holding his hand high in the air he then cried (in French), 'We are all in the shit up to *there*!' After a moment of stunned silence, even German officers in the audience were seen to laugh.

After the government fled Paris, chaos reigned in French official circles. France was occupied in the north and west and the country's intelligence service, never very strong on the ground, fell into disarray. When Pétain's government settled in Bordeaux, Abtey's counter-espionage post moved to the Loire region and then to Marseilles. There, under Captain Paul Paillole, head of Military Counter-espionage, the French Intelligence Service was reorganised to coordinate action against the enemy in France and North Africa. Paillole adopted the role of a rural development consultant and his staff became 'engineers' visiting towns and villages. The eventual seeds of the resistance were sown.

Still in Paris, Abtey was pleased with Josephine's information gathering and decided to continue working with her. As a French patriot, he deplored the collaboration policy of the Pétain regime. (Abtey's grandfather had been shot by the Germans in 1870, and he had been considered a German citizen until he was twelve, when Alsace and Lorraine were restored to France after the 1918 victory.) His allegiance was firmly with France suffering under the oppressor. To facilitate his work, Abtey assumed American nationality and the name of Fox.

Josephine for her part was shocked by what she learned of Nazi racism and discrimination against blacks. She was disillusioned by the Germany she had known in the 1920s, and offered to throw in her lot with Abtey. Abandoning her home in Le Vésinet and her stage and film commitments, they decided to leave for the chateau Josephine had leased in the Dordogne Valley, just beyond the zone occupied by the German forces. There, Abtey, alias Fox, gathered a dozen trusted colleagues round him to plan their future operations.

Almost at the same time, a recently promoted French army general, called to occupy an administrative post in the government, chose another route. Charles de Gaulle left Bordeaux for London to set up a mission to 'kindle the flame of French resistance'. A new epoch for France was about to begin.

In London, the British leader, Winston Churchill, formally received de Gaulle and put the BBC's Overseas Service at his disposal to address his compatriots. Listeners who were able to pick up the broadcasts were invited to rally to the Free French Forces and to give help where it was needed.

It was in the seclusion of the chateau in Milandes that Josephine, Abtey and their fellow FFF members began to hear de Gaulle's twice-weekly rallying call from London.

'Whatever happens,' declared de Gaulle at the microphone, 'the flame of the French resistance must not, and will not be extinguished.'*

The song of the partisans, with its insistent refrain, was soon to symbolise the determination of the 'freedom fighters' to liberate France from the invader. Josephine was joined by the Jewish family of her ex-husband, Jean Lion, seeking to escape the risk of deportation.

Abtey's plan was to join de Gaulle in London in order to be part of the centralised movement of the Free French Forces. Movement out of France was difficult and all the frontiers were guarded. Josephine was still in touch with impresarios in Portugal and South America. Under the pretext of planning new theatrical tours, Josephine and Abtey hoped to reach London by way of Spain and Portugal, countries still officially neutral in the

---

* 'La flamme de la Résistance française ne doit pas s'éteindre et ne s'éteindra pas.' – Charles de Gaulle.

European conflict.

Abtey, who had briefly become 'Jack Saunders' in Milandes, changed his name once more to Jacques-Francois Hébert, born 16 September 1899, in Marseilles, artiste by profession. False identity papers now gave his age as just over forty, avoiding the interdiction against younger men leaving the country. Glasses and a moustache completed the transformation from a known counter-espionage personality to an innocuous secretary. There was an added refinement: in a reversal of roles, Monsieur Hébert became the loyal assistant and ballet master to Miss Josephine Baker, the international star. In Intelligence language, Josephine was Abtey's 'cover', while he was in fact her 'controller'.

With a false passport, Hébert, alias Abtey, accompanied by Josephine, left by train for Spain. Despite frontier checks, all eyes were on Josephine, with hardly a glance at the shabby-looking Monsieur Hébert. Their decision to take the plane to Portugal presented new risks. German military personnel in Spain were already scrutinising travellers, looking for important refugees. Once again Josephine dazzled officials with her smile while Monsieur Hébert discreetly carried her luggage. Josephine's flamboyant manner excited so much attention that Abtey passed almost unobserved.

On 23 November 1940, Josephine and Abtey arrived in Lisbon in great style. They found a city in which German, French and British secret agents and businessmen rubbed shoulders and met in the same bars and restaurants, yet were ready to fight each other to the death in the war in the north. The port was the meeting place of Allied and Axis secret agents enjoying the neutrality of the country to conduct their clandestine operations. Informers and arms traders conducted deals in a unique atmosphere of connivance; the French preferred their own language while the Germans favoured English. Beneath the formal, bland exterior to every conversation, there lurked intense calculation and suspicion.

Abtey quietly took a room in the Avenida Palace Hotel while Josephine caused a sensation when she checked into the Aviz Hotel. Journalists who were tired of accosting tight-lipped known agents, crowded the foyer of the Aviz Hotel seeking anecdotes of

Josephine's journey from France.

'Yes, I am en route for Rio to fulfil an engagement,' Josephine replied a dozen times. 'I saw many sad sights in France... No, I have not returned to Paris since the occupation... No, I don't like the Germans...'

Abtey revealed himself to the British Ambassador in Lisbon and explained the reason for their presence in the capital. Abtey was able to pass on to British Intelligence details of the German army's strength in western France and their activities in ports and airfields that could be used to launch a possible attack on Gibraltar. The figures and locations had been concealed in coded music scores as part of Josephine's luggage carried by 'Mr Hébert'. Abtey asked for a passage to be arranged for Josephine and himself to join de Gaulle in London.

Four days later, the reply came back through British Intelligence sources in Lisbon; London was pleased to renew contact with members of the French Deuxième Bureau. They were to set up an intelligence network in Casablanca that would embrace the whole of North Africa. First, though, it should be rooted in the unoccupied zone of the French mainland, before extending to North Africa and the Middle East.

Josephine resigned herself to returning to Marseilles alone while Abtey prudently waited in Lisbon. Many like him were in a limbo of uncertainty, waiting for visas and watching the war from afar. Like many other agents and refugees, they found themselves caught up in an unreal world on the edge of a growing armed world conflict.

Back in Marseilles, Josephine found the country traumatised by the occupation and in the grip of a bitterly cold winter. When she reported to Colonel Paillole and mentioned their money problems, having spent so much on train and air fares, Paillole suggested Josephine put on a performance at the Municipal Theatre to raise funds while waiting for Abtey with fresh instructions from London.

At first, Josephine refused to go back on the stage saying, 'As long as there are Germans in France, I will not sing!' But when Paillole reasoned with her that her appearance would indirectly hasten their eventual departure, she agreed to appear. Also in

Marseilles at that moment, a former colleague from the Folies
Bergère made his appearance. Josephine was delighted to meet the
dancer Frédéric Rey, and together they decided to put on a revival
of *La Créole*, presented in Paris in 1934. Rey, who was Austrian-
born, was anxious to avoid identification by the Nazis. Josephine
recognised the danger for him and insisted that he leave France
for North Africa.

La Créole's Revival

From December 1940, the people of Marseilles were surprised to
see advertised a two-week revival of Jacques Offenbach's *La Créole*
at the local Opera House, featuring Josephine Baker. Those who
attended the hastily assembled production would have been
surprised to learn that the well-known music hall star appearing
before them was one of the first accredited members of the Free
French Forces (No. 18116). As the new production got under
way, Abtey returned to Marseilles with the news that he and
Josephine were to set up a liaison service with London, based in
Morocco, with a view to rallying France's North African
territories to the Free French Forces against Pétain's
collaborationist government in Vichy. All secret information
between the FFF and London would be handled by sea routes
between Lisbon and England. A small cargo vessel sailing under a
Portuguese flag was to be part of the operation. The apparently
devious route was necessary to assure absolute secrecy of the
information transmitted between France, North Africa and
London.

A new crisis then arose when Colonel Paillole informed Abtey
that the German forces were preparing to invade the remainder of
unoccupied France and that they should leave the country
immediately for their own safety and to assure the projected
establishment of their North African operation.

Josephine's exceptional one-night appearances in nearby
Béziers and Montpellier were hastily cancelled and a medical
certificate was produced explaining the sudden suspension of her
appearance in *La Créole*, due to pneumonia. It was not an
unreasonable excuse in view of the severe weather that winter.

As German advance parties approached the Mediterranean

coast, Josephine, Abtey and Rey, accompanied by a small menagerie of animals, set sail for Algeria aboard the *Gouverneur Général Gueydon*. In spite of their rapid departure, Josephine had assembled some of her pets from Milandes. Her personal belongings now included a Danish mastiff, a long-tailed monkey, a marmoset and two white mice! The accompanying menagerie was a part of her 'innocent' role as artiste.

A surprise awaited Josephine in Algiers. A police inspector presented her with a demand for 400,000 French francs damages for breach of contract with the Marseilles Opera Company for the sudden cancellation of *La Créole*. She would not be allowed to proceed to Morocco unless she settled the demand.

While Marseilles newspapers wrote of the 'scandalous departure of Miss Baker…' Josephine took it in her stride. She had been sued before; how could they know the imperative reason for her abrupt departure? After a week of urgent exchanges with Paillole, the demand was lifted and Josephine was free to move.

During her enforced wait for a transit visa, Josephine gave a benefit performance for French airmen in Algiers, while Abtey flew to Casablanca to prepare the next stage of their mission. There, their personal situation was reversed; while Josephine was free to move back through Spain to Portugal, Abtey (the faithful Monsieur Hébert) found himself blocked without the necessary papers to return to Europe. Josephine was left alone carrying her music scores that concealed details of German troop movements in southern France collected by Paillole and his associates in Marseilles. It was her first solo mission.

Arriving in Tangiers, in northern Morocco, Josephine renewed her acquaintance with members of the ruling Moroccan family, including Larbi Alaouï, cousin of the Sultan. Josephine was received by Thami El Ghaoui, the respected Pacha of Morocco and also his cousin, Mohammed Menebhi, whom she had met during the filming on location of *Tam-Tam*. He immediately offered her comfortable quarters in a traditional house in the medina quarter of Marrakech. Josephine was reminded that Moulay Larbi had visited the Folies Bergère Theatre in Paris in 1937 and was known for his pro-French sentiments.

Josephine was soon joined by Abtey who persuaded her to make a working visit to Spain, taking in Seville, Madrid and Barcelona. Josephine gave impromptu performances and attended social gatherings. The tour was made without incident and once again Josephine proved her ability to move freely without arousing suspicion in the minds of those she met. She collected valuable information in conversation with Spanish officials and rejoined Abtey in Morocco.

Chaos and Confusion

From 1940, the war in Europe became a world conflict. Hitler declared war on the United States; Japan invaded Indo-China and then joined the Rome-Berlin Axis powers. In Africa, Britain and her allies prepared to launch an offensive against the Italians in the Western Desert and confront Rommel's Afrika Korps.

As accredited members of the Free French Forces, Josephine and Abtey had to deal with complicated administrative problems related to their mission, between the various information services of the Allies. There were also several conflicting opinions over the involvement of Morocco in the conflict.

By the end of 1940, there were five separate British Intelligence sections attempting to conduct joint operations with the French. The two pre-war French Intelligence organisations, the Deuxième Bureau and the Service de Renseignements, were to be replaced by one, headed by de Gaulle in London. It was to become the Bureau Central de Renseignements et d'Action (BCRA). (The eventual head of BCRA, Captain André Dewavrin, became well known as 'Colonel Passy'.)

Waiting in Marrakech to unify their activities, Josephine and Abtey were first occupied with local problems. The situation between rival political and military factions was confused and evolving daily. Rommel's forces were reported to be advancing in Libya and there was fear that Spanish-German troops might attempt to infiltrate Morocco. The entry of the United States into the war was anxiously awaited; an advance guard of American officials was obliged to deal with pro-Vichy Moroccans while discreetly courting supporters of de Gaulle's Free French partisans.

Underlying the efforts of the Allies to conduct the war against the Axis powers, the situation in Morocco was further complicated by the rivalry between de Gaulle and General Giraud. Giraud had been named Commander in Chief of the French forces in North Africa and shared with de Gaulle the leadership of the CFLN, the French Committee of National Liberation.

As the German invasion forces spread throughout the French mainland, the French Intelligence Chief, Paillole, now calling himself Monsieur Perrier, left occupied France for Morocco to set up a new counter-espionage post in Casablanca to be headed by Abtey.

Illness Strikes Josephine

In June 1941, Josephine suffered acute internal pains. A doctor diagnosed peritonitis and advised her to enter a clinic immediately in Casablanca, better equipped than those in Marrakech. Aided by Abtey, she travelled overnight to the northern port and was admitted to the clinic of Dr Henri Comte.

There are several versions of Josephine's illness and subsequent series of surgical operations. Due in part to the confidential nature of Josephine's mission, the cause of her hospitalisation remains unclear. There were suggestions that the origin of her illness was a miscarriage. Some commentators even suggested it was a case of poisoning by women jealous of Josephine's familiarity with her Moroccan hosts in Marrakech.

Perhaps the most reliable source is contained in Jacques Abtey's published memoirs. He recounts Josephine's medical consultation in Casablanca and subsequent abdominal pain, diagnosed as peritonitis, and attributes this to an infection from an injection by the X-ray consultant. Abtey recalls that it was Josephine's desire to have children of her own after the war that caused her to seek medical consultation. And he confirms that Josephine was hospitalised in Casablanca from June 1941 until December 1942.

Despite her hospitalisation in Casablanca, Josephine's bedside had become an unofficial meeting place of personalities and well-wishers of many nationalities. Pro-French Moroccans and other allies were able to discuss the future possible landing of an American expeditionary force in North Africa. An innocent question to an official often revealed information on future political or military strategy which was promptly noted by Abtey and his growing team of informers. One of her early visitors was the American Vice-Consul in Rabat, who had come to pay his respects to a compatriot.

Josephine refused to receive one unexpected visitor from Paris. Maurice Chevalier later told journalists that Josephine was 'dying penniless in a Moroccan hospital'. The erroneous report reproduced worldwide provoked a wave of sympathy and offers of help from abroad. Josephine later told Abtey that 'Chevalier was a great artiste but a small man'.

The War in North Africa

While the world conflict unfolded on all fronts, 1942 saw a turning point in North Africa when American and British troops landed on the Moroccan and Algerian coasts, supported by British sea and air forces. Morocco was still a protectorate of the French Vichy Government and the mixed local populations were deeply divided over involvement in the war. The arrival of American troops provoked several days of armed clashes in Casablanca and there were protest demonstrations against the Allied expeditionary force.

Josephine insisted on viewing the arrival of the American troops from the roof of the hospital. She then moved back to the Palace of Mohammed Menebhi in Marrakech to complete her convalescence in the Atlas foothills. She had been warned not to undertake unnecessary physical effort.

Even during her hospitalisation, Josephine had been flown to neighbouring Algiers for a brief appearance at the French Fête d'Aviation. She sang for an hour before being returned to her sickbed and claimed that the effort had contributed to her eventual recovery.

As the war raged throughout the Mediterranean, with Allied forces gaining ground against the Axis powers, Josephine was invited to help maintain the morale of the expeditionary forces, under the banner of the Cross of Lorraine, symbol of the French Liberation under de Gaulle.

Josephine rediscovered members of her own race when she was invited to inaugurate the Liberty Club for black soldiers in Casablanca. Despite their equality under the Constitution, the American army maintained racial segregation. Half a million black Americans were mobilised in the war but it was said that their only true integration was in combat and death. (Desegregation of the US armed forces only took place in 1948 under President Truman.)

Tour of North Africa and the Middle East

From 1943, Josephine was personally co-opted by British and American military leaders in Marrakech to tour Allied military camps in North Africa and the Middle East. Organised jointly by ENSA, the Entertainers National Services Association, and the parallel USO American service, her mission was to help maintain the morale of tens of thousands of armed men stationed in combat zones or in reserve, waiting to go into action.

Josephine refused payment for her scheduled appearances, asking only that transport, food and accommodation be supplied wherever she was sent. Accompanied by the dancer, Frédéric Rey, and a group of chosen black musicians, the troupe was managed by Fernand Zimmer, Abtey's Alsatian colleague. Mohammed Menabhi joined the expedition as interpreter.

Josephine's new mission took her to a dozen different countries of the Maghreb and the Middle East. Travelling in a convoy of jeeps with occasional airlifts, the troupe covered more than 3,000 miles between Casablanca and Damascus.

It was a very different kind of operation from Josephine's peacetime tours. Conditions were hard, with long motorised treks to distant camp sites. The exercise reminded her of her early tours of the United States when an uncertain welcome often awaited her troupe. The tour began in the West Algerian region of Oran, where some 300,000 British, Australian and French men were on active service. Their arrival created a sensation.

Conditions varied greatly from camp to camp and country to country, according to the local environment and the course of the war. Production facilities were scarce or non-existent and Josephine and Rey often appeared on makeshift stages, sometimes lit by anti-aircraft searchlights. They shared the lifestyle of troops, eating and sleeping under canvas. Josephine's companions supported her efforts to bring some entertainment to soldiers living in isolated regions waiting to go into action.

A feature of their performance was the unfurling of a huge French flag embellished with the Cross of Lorraine as a finale. Since the First World War the emblem had also been known as the Cross of the Liberation. Josephine's energy and determination as a fervent Gaullist surprised those she met and helped to convince them of the justice of the Allied cause.

The tour was not without incident. In Algiers, their performance was suddenly interrupted when enemy planes strafed the camp they were visiting, and they had to take cover urgently. In Cairo, Josephine refused to sing impromptu for King Farouk at a Franco-Egyptian reception because Egypt had not yet officially recognised de Gaulle's Provisional French Government. (After General Giraud's resignation in August 1944, de Gaulle was the undisputed leader of the Free French Forces.) The presence of Allied troops in Middle Eastern countries had revealed latent colonial rivalries, notably in Egypt, Lebanon and Syria.

In Beirut, Lebanon, Josephine raised 350,000 French francs for the Resistance, by auctioning the precious little gold Cross of Lorraine that de Gaulle had personally given her when they had met in Algiers. In Ajaccio, Corsica, Josephine, Rey and the musicians were acclaimed by thousands of soldiers and civilians on 31 May in the main square of the island capital. It was Josephine's first return to French soil after nearly three years. During the intervening months Josephine had been officially enlisted as a sub-lieutenant in the women's division of the French Air Force.

The Liberation of Paris

By August 1944, the Allies had gained the initiative in Europe and the liberation of Paris was only a matter of days. General Leclerc's Armoured Division, formed at Lake Chad in Central Africa three years earlier, had crossed the Sahara to join the 8th Army in the

Africa campaign. Leclerc was at the gates of Paris waiting for final orders.

On 23 August, the insurrection against the occupiers of Paris intensified. There was shooting from the rooftops and fear among the population. The German Commander of the Paris Garrison, General von Choltz, defied Hitler's orders to destroy the city. On 25 August 1944, Leclerc's Armoured Division entered Paris through the Orleans Gate, to be acclaimed by the populace. Leclerc personally received the surrender of the German general, and the bells of Notre-Dame Cathedral and every church in the capital tolled the news of the Liberation of Paris.

When the President of the National French Resistance asked de Gaulle to proclaim the Republic, he replied, 'No! The Republic has never ceased to exist!'

After the Liberation

If Josephine had been asked what she had done during the war, it was not certain what she would have replied. She rarely spoke of it after she had received decorations for her services, but she occasionally appeared on official occasions proudly wearing her uniform of a sub-lieutenant in the Women's Division of the French Air Force.

The citations for her awards were brief. Many more of those who had risked their lives, or perished in daring sabotage operations against the enemy, remained unnamed after the Liberation. The details of Josephine's activities in the Resistance remained largely undocumented until her companion, Captain Jacques Abtey, published his *Secret War of Josephine Baker*. It contained a personal letter to Josephine from President Charles de Gaulle, who wrote,

> I send you my sincere congratulations for the high distinction of the French Resistance you have received. I fully appreciate the great services you have given in those most difficult times... and to have put your magnificent talent at the disposal of our cause...
>
> Charles de Gaulle

Josephine's devotion to the Allied cause in the Second World War stands out as a unique contribution from a profession not noted for its militancy. Many theatrical performers continued to entertain their French compatriots and the enemy alike during the occupation. Some female artistes openly consorted with German officers, claiming that their personal liberty outweighed any patriotic obligations. Maurice Chevalier later found himself having to defend his appearance in a prisoner of war camp in Germany. While the war raged in North Africa in 1942, Mistinguett was performing at the Casino de Paris. The question of who did what during the Occupation remains a delicate subject.

In Josephine's case, one thing is certain; during the war she suffered a great deal, not from direct enemy action but from personal sacrifice and illness. As an American-born naturalised French performer, she had no obligation to offer her services. Like that other artiste, Mistinguett, she was too well known to conceal her true identity to become a spy. Due to her celebrity, her information gathering was indirect and casual but concealed a shrewdness and self-discipline.

The private dramas of her illnesses and obstinacy in carrying on against medical advice gave Josephine's war effort a special piquancy. This *métisse* from Missouri, who exemplified a mixture of racial and cultural origins, found her natural vocation in helping to fight racial discrimination. The war had offered her a challenge and had revealed qualities hitherto hidden to her fans and admirers. She suffered physically but never weakened in her resolve to acquit herself of her newly adopted role.

Despite the ending of hostilities and the Liberation of Paris, Josephine's tour of duty was not finished. She was officially commissioned to visit units of the French First Army in freed territories to continue her mission of maintaining the morale of the troops. She quickly co-opted the band leader, Joseph Bouillon, and together with a chosen group of musicians they set off. The tour took in France but soon extended to Germany, Scandinavia and North Africa.

Josephine was in top form, welcoming the return of peace and proclaiming the justice of the Allied effort. She had never wavered in her loyalty to de Gaulle and French independence. It was also for Josephine a new stage in her personal life; her professional association with Jo Bouillon was destined to lead to marriage.

Top: Josephine Baker in the uniform of the women's auxillary service of the French Airforce, wearing her medals of the Resistance.

Coll. Diaz, archives départmentales de la Dordogne.

Bottom: In her first sound film Josephine played opposite Jean Gabin in *ZouZou*, directed by Marc Allégret in 1934.

At her last appearance in Paris in 1975, Josephine astonished audiences with her youthful performance.

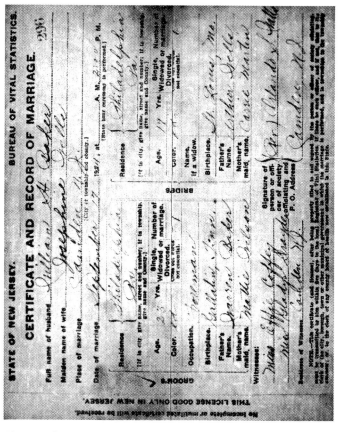

The certificate and record of marriage in Philadelphia, New Jersey, in 1921, when Josephine claimed to be nineteen years old, reveals the origin of the name Baker.

Josephine in Buenos Aires, Argentina.

Top: Josephine's image from the 20s adorns a central Paris Metro station for the celebration of the bicentenary of the French Republic. *Bottom:* The French Postal Authority, the PTT, paid homage to Josephine Baker among other theatrical personalities, in a special edition of stamps in 1984.

Reproduced by kind permission of Musée de la Poste, Paris.

Josephine Baker with her husband Jo, in company with the
painter Maurice Vlaminck at Reuil-La-Gadelière, France.
Musée des beaux-arts de Chartres, France, coll. privée.

Top left: The Chateau of 'Les Milandes', in south-west France became the home of the Rainbow Tribe of adopted orphans.
Top right: Song titles often recalled Josephine's childhood in Saint-Louis.
Bottom: Josephine's chaste 'new look' in the 1930s adorned the programme of the Casino de Paris designed by Zig.

A family reunion of the Rainbow Tribe at the chateau of Milandes – Josephine and husband Jo and some of the family, including, from left in front row: Akio, Jean-Claude, Koffi, Janot.

Coll. Roger-Viollet.

Chapter Seven

The Story of Milandes and the Stork Club Affair

In 1946 Josephine was well off, famous, and the owner of two homes in Paris and a chateau in south-west France. She was also at an age when irresistible urges impelled her to change direction in her life. With her wartime exploits behind her, a return to her pre-war existence of endless tours now seemed less attractive; retirement from the stage would free her for other activities, one of which had been germinating in her mind for many years. At forty Josephine was ready to embark on a project that many people acknowledge in retrospect was fraught with difficulties. It came to be known as Milandes.

Josephine had played many different roles in her private and professional life; chorus line clown, dissident black activist, international star and loyal member of the French Resistance. She was now ready to play a part that had been denied her until now – that of mother to a family of adopted children.

It is not known when Josephine first conceived the idea of founding a family of adopted children and of creating a multiracial community. Years of experience of discrimination and intolerance, coupled with personal humiliation, had left their mark. The chagrin of realising, after serious illnesses, that she could not have children of her own, may have finally convinced her to adopt some orphans. Whatever it was, circumstances now combined to offer her the possibility of founding a family and of demonstrating how racial harmony could be achieved if begun at an early age. France had given her the possibility of proclaiming racial equality. Now at last she could put to good use the chateau she had leased since before the war.

The dream of universal brotherhood was a simplistic ideal

nurtured in Josephine from early childhood. To mollify the family's fears of rampaging whites in St. Louis, their father had evoked a future 'Golden Age', when whites and blacks would live in harmony together. The preacher in church had brandished the threat of 'fire and brimstone' as the penalty for not loving those who sinned against you, and held out the promise of a distant paradise of universal love as the prize. For Josephine the creation of such paradise on earth would be vindication of her own unhappy childhood spent in the black ghetto of Boxcar Town in St. Louis.

Now began the third most remarkable, and painful, period of Josephine's life. With Jo Bouillon her orchestra leader, with whom she had toured at the end of the war, she set in motion an experiment in living that would affect the lives of scores of people. They would include members of her own family from America, the local village population around her chateau, and a future family of adopted orphans.

The story of Milandes began innocently enough when Josephine had been touring the French countryside with her first French husband, Jean Lion, in 1937. Exploring the lush Dordogne Valley region near Sarlat, they took a leafy lane beside the river and came upon the turrets and roofs of a small chateau rising above the treetops. For Josephine it was a moment of revelation, a dream of childhood, a fairy-tale castle come to life.

The chateau stood on high ground overlooking the River Dordogne and was surrounded by small farms and cottages in some 600 acres of rich agricultural land. The district was originally known by the Occitan word, 'Mirandes', meaning viewpoint. The chateau was built in 1489 by François de Caumont, Baron of Castelnaud, a nearby village and fortified castle. The edifice remained in the Caumont family until the Revolution, when it was spared destruction by faithful retainers. It was later sold at public auction and had several owners, including a Monsieur Claverie, who added a small wing and laid out gardens and terraces.

Although the casement windows and sculpted gables beneath the crenellated towers remained largely unchanged throughout the years, time had caught up with the chateau, and between the wars it fell into disrepair and was abandoned. Despite the fact that its solid walls had stood for centuries, its isolation discouraged permanent occupation. When Josephine discovered Milandes, it needed new fittings and modern services to make its twenty rooms habitable. The overgrown gardens and deserted adjoining hamlet required a workforce to bring the land back to productivity. Owing to its dilapidated condition the lease had been easily acquired, but the building had remained empty during the war, except for secret meetings between French and Allied Resistance leaders. Milandes and its surroundings were now ripe for rehabilitation.

Spread between the central high lands and the Atlantic coast, the region is rich in historical associations. The more Josephine learned about the district, the more she became convinced of the tourist potential waiting to be exploited. Her ideas were nothing if not big, and her enthusiasm carried her imagination to new heights; already it began to embrace the whole area.

'It's very simple,' she insisted, 'Périgord is already a first-class tourist centre. Tomorrow it could become a paradise for rich summer visitors, and a source of revenue for the region, if one knows how to attract and keep foreign visitors.'

Milandes was also near the Panassou natural spring at Castel, whose waters allegedly contained minerals said by the villagers to be 'thirty times more potent than the mud at Dax', a reference to the health centre in the south-west. Seizing on this information, Josephine exclaimed, 'With these miraculous waters of youth at our door, we'll never grow old!'

The region is also rich in fossil and prehistoric remains, notably the cave paintings at Lascaux. This further endeared the district to Josephine who felt that such vestiges of the past were good omens for the future. Her vision of Milandes as a world centre for young people embraced the past. To all who would listen she enthused, 'I've discovered that this region was considered by knowledgeable people to be the centre of humanity in prehistoric times. What a coincidence!'

Coincidence or not, there was work to be done. The focal point of Josephine's plan was the adoption of children; she and Jo Bouillon had agreed that four would be the ideal number. The young family would include a white and a black child, and an Indian and an Asian would complete the quartet. As Josephine put it, it would be a 'Rainbow Tribe' of orphans of different colours; white, black, brown and yellow. The adopted family would inhabit the chateau, around which would grow a commercial holiday centre with tourist attractions to sustain the estate and help pay for its development and support the family.

The plan was ambitious and included the creation of two hotels, restaurants, a swimming pool (estimated to cost 25 million francs), two tennis courts, a miniature golf course, with alleys for French bowls or pétanque. In addition there would be an open-air theatre, a museum, a small zoo, a playground for children, and a garage and parking space for no less than one hundred visiting cars and coaches. A casino was also a distant project.

With French nationality from her earlier marriage, Josephine would encounter no legal or administrative barriers in developing Milandes as a business venture. Jo Bouillon was the ideal and willing partner for the enterprise; Josephine's lofty idealism needed only the steadying hand of careful management. With Josephine's celebrity and taste for publicity, the combination of their two talents seemed to provide the right basis for creating a family home supported by a tourist complex. It remained only for Josephine and Jo to marry to form the ideal partnership.

Jo Bouillon married Josephine on 3 June 1947 in a Catholic ceremony conducted by the village priest who celebrated Mass each Sunday in the private chapel attached to the chateau. Villagers from the surrounding district crowded into the tiny building and the congregation included the Bouillon family on the bridegroom's side, while Pepito's sister, Christine, and members of the Scotto family represented Josephine's absent parents.

The civil formalities of the marriage were carried out at the offices of the local mayor of the commune of Castelnaud-Feyrac. Josephine's name appears on the register as Joséphine Freda Baker, daughter of Arthur Baker and Carrie McDonald, divorced from Jean Lion. (Baker was in fact Josephine's name from her second marriage to William H Baker, in America in 1921.)

Shortly after their marriage, Josephine acquired full legal

ownership of the Milandes chateau and estate with its park bordering the river, and she became the 'chatelaine' of the hamlet. She sold her mansion in the Paris suburb of Le Vésinet, and her apartment in the capital, and established a new home in Milandes.

As teams of workmen moved in, the fifteenth-century chateau came to life; carpenters, plumbers, painters and electricians began transforming the solid stone structure into a home with modern facilities. Fully appointed bathrooms were added to each of the twelve bedrooms. Carpets were laid in the reception rooms. Stonemasons repaired and cleaned staircases and exterior walls. The adjoining grounds were landscaped and replanted with flowers.

A number of families took up residence in the adjoining hamlet to cultivate market garden produce and raise livestock. Josephine aspired to be self-sufficient in locally grown food and even envisaged producing a wine with her name on the label to be called 'Chateau Milandes'. Jo, for his part, found himself one of the biggest landowners in the region, with prime cattle herds, poultry and a small staff of employees.

Many helpers around the estate saw the enterprise as a lucrative source of occupation, and imagined the new owners to have unlimited funds. 'Wasn't Josephine Baker one of the highest paid international stars,' they said, 'and a former officer in the French Resistance, someone whose credit was good?'

Local tradespeople from nearby villages began to supply products and services, hoping to benefit from the largesse that would flow from the combined resources of these 'city folk with ideas', and help of local expertise.

Despite her dedication to the task or restoring Milandes and developing the estate, Josephine was still a long way from giving up the stage. Agents and impresarios in many countries continued to suggest tours or special appearances. Together with Jo she discussed which proposal would be most beneficial. Where possible Jo and his orchestra would accompany her; their joint appearances would keep Josephine's name before the public and help defray the costs of developing the estate.

When Jo could not accompany her because of radio commitments in Paris, Josephine would tour with Pierre Spiers, a talented musician, composer and orchestra leader. Pierre Spiers wrote a song for Josephine entitled 'When I Think of That'. It was a thoughtful ballad of the woes of the world that became part of her repertoire. 'It was a message she wanted to give,' explained Spiers. 'It fitted exactly with her ideas and character.'

Josephine's ideas and character were also becoming revealed as the Milandes enterprise grew in complexity and size. Despite being called away on tour, Josephine wanted a hand in everything. This often conflicted with Jo's efforts to bring some order into the running of the estate. Jo's instructions were frequently countermanded by the unexpected reappearance of Josephine from a distant engagement. This confused the employees, who either took advantage of the conflict of authority or simply left.

Almost as though the war years had been an unwanted interruption in her career, Josephine resumed her stage appearances, hopping from capital to capital like a veteran diplomat, flashing her famous smile, answering reporters' questions, and going through her practised routine on stage. Her act had hardly changed and her performances varied little. She danced less, sang more, and talked a lot...

Her wartime experiences had broadened her knowledge of how people lived, and died. Now she had a certain authority in telling people about life's injustices, and her recipe for putting the world to rights. At the slightest opportunity, she would expound on the theme of universal brotherhood.

'The unity of children of different countries is the best way of countering discrimination, of fostering understanding, freedom and peace between different people of the world,' she would continually declare. So Josephine went back on the road again, campaigning for the cause that had become her raison d'être.

Family Reunion

In 1948 Josephine's widowed mother, Carrie Martin McDonald, and her sister Margarette with her husband Elmo Wallace, arrived in Milandes. They had been persuaded to emigrate to France and join Josephine in her village. Carrie was bewildered by the life Josephine led and the authority she wielded in Milandes, but they all fell in with helping to create the tourist centre.

Margarette opened a pastry shop; brother Richard and his young son, Arthur, who followed him from St. Louis, took over the village filling station. Richard later married the local post-mistress and together they were responsible for a small sub-post office in Milandes.

Josephine saw things falling into place as she would have wished; her brother's marriage to Marie-Louise seemed to demonstrate her thesis of interracial harmony. For her part, Marie-Louise said it was her way of helping Josephine who, she said, 'does so much to bring the races together'.

The Stork Club Affair

Of the many clashes between Josephine and the United States authorities over racial questions, the 'Stork Club Affair' remains the most celebrated and painful for those concerned. It began from a mundane incident in a New York restaurant and escalated to provoke nationwide comment and involve top administrators.

In October 1951 Josephine was appearing at the Roxy Theatre in New York and was one of a party of four to visit the exclusive, and expensive, Stork Club, on the East 53rd Street. The party was hosted by Roger Rico, the French singer starring in *South Pacific*, accompanied by his wife, and Bessie Buchanan, a dancer. The four arrived in high spirits about midnight to dine and ordered drinks. A bottle of French wine was promptly served. The food was to follow.

Among the many customers present when they arrived was the influential radio and press columnist, Walter Winchell, who was a friend of the club's owner, Sherman Billingsley. Winchell, who had written admiringly about Josephine in the past, occupied his usual table and acknowledged Josephine when she arrived.

After apparently being ignored by the waiters for more than half an hour, Roger Rico, who was also known to the club's owner, complained about the delay, only to be told that there was no food left! Josephine immediately interpreted the delay and refusal to serve their table as discrimination against her and Rico's wife and her friend, who were also both black. They pleaded with Josephine to ignore the apparent insult, but to no avail. Josephine went to telephone the NAACP* and the police, to lodge a formal complaint against the club, for discourtesy and discrimination and for being kept waiting for nearly an hour for food they had requested.

When Josephine returned to their table she observed that Winchell had disappeared from the room. When a small steak was finally brought to their table, Roger Rico angrily decided they should leave and called for the bill. This was refused because it was explained 'celebrities are not charged'. Mr Rico paid $30 and the party left the club.

The next day the incident became public knowledge when newspapers reported Josephine's complaint. As the story grew Josephine told reporters that Walter Winchell, who was present in the club at a nearby table, did nothing to intervene on their behalf. She added that she would picket the Stork Club on the grounds that it discriminated against Negroes.

The French Consul in New York immediately tried to dissuade Josephine from such a demonstration, but pickets appeared, including among them her fellow guest, Bessie Buchanan, moving silently up and down outside the Stork Club entrance.

The NAACP Executive Secretary, Walter White, meanwhile called on the State to intervene on the basis of civil rights law (which effectively prohibits discrimination by a restaurant on racial or religious grounds). The State Alcoholic Beverages Board was also asked to examine the business side of the Stork Club. Billingsley was known to have a long history linked to bootlegging illegal liquor.

As the temperature mounted, Walter Winchell entered the fray to deplore what he saw as attempts to involve him in an incident in which he had played no active part. On his regular Sunday-night radio programme, and in his weekly press column, syndicated nationwide, Winchell stressed his ignorance of the incident. He said he was 'appalled at the agony and embarrassment caused Josephine Baker and her friends at the Stork Club', but he stopped short of condemning Billingsley's

---

* The National Association for the Advancement of Coloured People.

attitude towards coloured or black customers.

The NAACP for its part demanded equal air time from the American Broadcasting Company to reply to Winchell and to give their point of view. As various factions and individuals began to take sides, Josephine's personal agent in New York, Curt Weinberg, resigned from representing her, because of embarrassment to him and his other clients. As news of the incident spread abroad, Jo Bouillon flew from Paris to be at his wife's side in the growing scandal.

Josephine's complaint against the Stork Club was not upheld by the authorities. A police investigation, including interviews with people said to have been present in the club on the night in question, concluded that 'the facts do not substantiate any charge and are insufficient to proceed against the Stork Club management in a criminal court'. The police report added that Sherman Billingsley said that he served people from all over the world but naturally gave preference to steady customers; the investigation had failed to reveal that Miss Baker or any member of her party had been refused service of food and beverages while in the club.

But that was not the end of the affair. The NAACP immediately described the Police Commissioner's report as 'a complete and shameless whitewash of the long-established and well-known discriminatory policies of the Stork Club'. It added that while there could be no criminal prosecution, the association would continue to press for redress before the State Liquor Authority and in the civil courts.

Walter Winchell, meanwhile, still aggrieved that his name and reputation had been dragged into the affair, began his own campaign of personal criticism of Josephine. Using all the considerable media resources at his disposal, he attempted to smear Josephine with allegations of inconsistency in her behaviour over the years.

The first salvo of his campaign was gleaned from a news story nearly twenty years old, in which Josephine had unwisely said she was in favour of Mussolini's invasion of Ethiopia, then called Abyssinia. The anecdote appeared in Winchell's weekly gossip column but it made little sense to most readers. It was only the beginning…

The McCarthy witch-hunts for suspected communist sympathisers in the US were then just beginning. As more people joined the picket line outside the Stork Club, now led by NAACP Executive Secretary, Walter White, Winchell tried to use the wave of public feeling to imply that Josephine was a tool of the communists. He claimed that some of the demonstrators were recognisably those who had taken part in the Peekskill riots that accompanied Paul Robeson's song recitals. (Robeson's pro-Soviet sympathies at the time were well known, and receipts from his concerts were given to the Harlem Chapter of the Civil Rights Congress.)

Winchell was aware that partisan feelings regarding Jews and Negroes often went hand in hand, since he was a Jew himself. He turned to Marcel Sauvage's *Mémoires de Joséphine Baker*, a new edition published in 1949, and devoted space in his column to imputing anti-Jewish sentiments to Josephine. But his supposed quotation was taken out of context, was misquoted, and mistranslated from the French. He was soon denounced in the press by those who troubled to analyse the original.

Winchell's reaction to the Stork Club incident was out of proportion since it was not the central issue. But his column was syndicated by the powerful Hearst Corporation and King Features to hundreds of newspapers across the nation and was read by millions. If his persistent smear campaign merely diminished the author, it also began to damage Josephine's chances of further work in the United States. Agents didn't want to handle potential troublemakers, and the Stork Club Affair had gone far enough. Something had to be done.

The lawsuit caused a new flurry of interest from the media. Arthur Garfield Hays, Josephine's lawyer, was a veteran campaigner in civil rights cases and was General Council to the American Civil Liberties Union. He stage-managed a special press conference to back up the claim for damages and told reporters, 'We would accept a complete retraction by Winchell, and payment of expenses. We are not out to make money.'

In response to Winchell's suggestion of Josephine's fascist sympathies, a surprise witness arrived by air from Casablanca.

Major Jacques Abtey, Josephine's former Resistance colleague during the war, was presented as a French officer of the Intelligence Service of the Free French Army. He testified that he had been Josephine's commanding officer until the end of the war and that she had been entrusted with a number of dangerous missions by the Allies, in their fight against fascism.

Hays also addressed a personal letter to Winchell in which he asked the columnist to confirm that the issue of race relations was far more important than differences between individuals. He received no reply.

Josephine's claim for $100,000 damages for loss of earnings, a quarter of the total sum demanded, was becoming a very real issue. Offers to appear in major cities had fallen off and Josephine was worried that Winchell's column had influenced managers against booking her. There was speculation that Winchell had gone further and used his influence regarding prospective engagements.

'We want to examine Winchell to see if he has confined his attacks to his column,' said Hays, in true courtroom manner.

The truth was that managers had become very cautious of engaging an artiste who might provoke an incident in public as Josephine had done. They did not need Winchell to tell them that it was bad for business. Meanwhile, Josephine was spending more time addressing civil rights gatherings than entertaining the public. They offered no fee but sometimes paid expenses. When Jo and her agent warned Josephine to stick to entertaining she was unrepentant, saying, 'I'm not mad at Winchell. I believe in love and brotherhood.'

After trying to reason with her, Jo flew back to France and Milandes to face the rising costs of the estate. A lucrative Hollywood film contract was said to have evaporated in the ensuing lawsuit.

Perhaps the nearest Josephine Baker came to making a film in Hollywood came in 1952 while she was appearing at Ciro's showplace on the Hollywood Strip. Her agent at that time, William Taub, was attempting to secure film offers for his client, and recounts a scarcely believable story of Josephine's unreasonableness which allegedly spoiled her chances of appearing with Marilyn Monroe in the film version of Anita Loos's stage comedy, *Gentlemen Prefer Blondes*.

According to Taub, Josephine and Marilyn had formed a friendship and it was Josephine who was the first of the two to be offered a role in the film with Betty Grable. She then reportedly asked for a part for Marilyn Monroe, and this was approved by the studio head, Darryl Zanuck.

Josephine then made the startling suggestion that the film should be re-titled 'Gentlemen Prefer Josephine Baker'! Josephine's contract was never signed; Marilyn Monroe rose to stardom in the film and was, according to Taub, ever grateful for Josephine's intervention on her behalf.

In no other account of Josephine's American tour is there any mention of such a film offer, and Josephine never refers to either Monroe or the incident. William Taub's later attempt to sue Josephine for $10,000 for his professional services as her exclusive agent may help to explain this barely credible anecdote.

Winchell Case Abandoned

The $400,000 lawsuit that Josephine had initiated remained unresolved for many months. Winchell continued to write his column and broadcast but his days on the air were numbered. Television was claiming a much larger audience than he had ever addressed on radio, and he was soon pensioned off by his employers. Finally, the court set a 30 June deadline in 1955, for action by the plaintiffs. None came and the case was dropped.

In the intervening time, Bessie Buchanan, one of the guests at the ill-fated supper party, became the first black woman to take her place in the New York Assembly. Later still, a young American actress at the start of her career revealed that she had been present in the Stork Club on the night of the famous incident. Grace Kelly had seen it all but at the time she had neither the know-how nor the influence to champion the victim of such humiliation. But as Princess Grace of Monaco she was later to prove her sympathy and active support for Josephine, at a time of supreme crisis.

More than twenty years later an article in the *New Yorker* magazine revealed perhaps why Walter Winchell had reacted so strongly against Josephine whom he had once publicly praised. The magazine wrote that, at the time of the Stork Club incident, Josephine was booked to appear in New York at a café theatre run by a certain Monte Proser. When she discovered how filthy the dressing rooms at the theatre were, she refused to appear. Proser and Winchell were, as that magazine put it, 'as thick as thieves'. Was it loyalty to Proser that caused Winchell to launch his vendetta? Wars have started for lesser reasons.

Adoptions

It was during her tours abroad that Josephine began to search for children for her mixed-race adopted family. After appearing at the Arc-en-Ciel cabaret in Saigon, during an Asian tour in 1953, she visited Japan for the first time. She had been invited to make some charity appearances in aid of the Elisabeth Saunders Home for Orphans in Tokyo. Her hostess was the wife of the Japanese Ambassador to France whom she had met in Paris.

During her visit to the home Josephine confided her family plans for Milandes. Her hosts were delighted when she decided to choose her first adopted child from amongst the Asian children at the orphanage. Responding to her hosts' interest, Josephine decided to adopt not one, but two infants: Akio, who had been abandoned by his Korean mother, and Janot, a Japanese child. Akio was born a Buddhist, while Janot belonged to Shinto. Both children were probably fathered by American servicemen.

Later the same year, on a visit to Finland, Josephine found Jari, who had been left in a Helsinki orphanage only one month before her visit. In contrast to his Asian brothers, Jari was blue-eyed and blond and a baptised Protestant. The three adopted infants were all barely two years old when they began their new life in France. A stranger destiny could hardly be imagined for the trio brought together under one roof in Milandes.

The fourth child to join the family was Luis, the eighth baby of a black mother in Colombia who had come to Josephine's hotel in Bogota. In exchange for the custody of her child Josephine gave the woman a large sum of money to help her house her already large family. The lawyer who arranged the adoption confirmed that there were no legal obstacles because the woman had voluntarily sought out Josephine to have her child adopted.

Josephine now had the number of adopted children agreed to with Jo, but it became clear to both of them that four was too small a number to accommodate the different races and religions she desired to compose her family. They quickly realised that a correct balance of skin colour with race and religion would be difficult – if not impossible – to achieve without enlarging the family.

Between 1954 and 1968 Josephine was to adopt eight more children than the original four planned with Jo. The circumstances of each adoption differed widely and procedures varied from country to country. Legal and emotional problems sometimes intervened but Josephine's motives and good faith were generally acknowledged, even when, in some cases, she was warned against breaking the law over adoptions in some countries.

In the young Republic of Israel, the authorities flatly refused to allow a Jewish child to be taken out of the country. A government official said that children are not given for adoption to people of other faiths, and Miss Baker was not Jewish. He said great efforts were made to bring children into the country and not to lose them. Josephine subsequently found a Jewish orphan through the French Welfare Services in Paris. Nine-month-old Moise, who had been cared for by a foster mother, quickly joined his Catholic, Shinto, Protestant and Buddhist brothers in Milandes.

In 1956 Josephine returned to North Africa and was fêted in towns she knew during the war. In Algiers the resident French minister took her to see two infants who had escaped the recent Palestro massacre. Too small to be noticed in the turmoil, they had been found wrapped up together under a tree. Little Marianne was Catholic and Brahim was a Muslim Berber. For Josephine there was no other course but to bring the two back home. At Milandes Jo was surprised; not only at being presented with two more infants, but at finding that one of them was a girl. They had earlier decided to adopt only boys.

At Christmas that year Josephine presided over the kind of family gathering she had dreamed about but never experienced.

Surrounded by her seven adopted children and family beside her, she distributed presents from a huge garlanded Christmas tree. The cries of wonderment and delight allowed Jo and his wife to momentarily put aside their concerns about running the estate and the number of unpaid bills. That Josephine could have brought together children of so many different cultures for a traditional Christian ceremony in a fourteenth-century chateau in the heart of the French countryside was an extraordinary achievement. The improbability of the occasion would stay in the memory of all those present.

The following year Josephine swept off again to Africa, this time to perform in the Ivory Coast capital of Abidjan. Within weeks she was back in France – with Koffi, a black African. The adopted family now numbered eight!

The growing family of infants required constant attention to help them adapt to the strange life they had been thrust into. Visitors to Milandes came to stare at the family as though they were an extension of the small zoo Josephine had set up in one wing of the chateau. The children tried to hide from the inquisitive tourists and their cameras.

When the children attended school there was no escape from outspoken local pupils and even their parents. Lessons were difficult in an atmosphere of tension and riotous horseplay. The children were glad to return to the relative shelter of their familiar dormitory in the chateau.

Finally Josephine felt obliged to withdraw them from school and to have them educated at home. But tutors were hard to find, and they had to be paid. At a time in their young lives when they needed understanding and a certain discipline, they were frequently taught by occasional tutors or abandoned to their own devices. They were living in isolated surroundings, cut off from the everyday world they would one day have to confront.

Such problems were known only to close observers or intimates of the family. A young French girl living nearby paid frequent visits to the estate. While playing with the children she remembers that they were perfectly happy together, living as she put it, 'in a kind of time warp', unaware of the real world beyond the limits of the chateau and its gardens.

Separation

In 1957 the inevitable happened. Since the end of the war the professional association between Josephine and Jo had been successful and their marriage had seemed a logical outcome of their collaboration at Milandes. But tension between them had been growing over the running of the estate, and friends close to them had noted signs of incompatibility. Some openly declared that Jo was 'not made for marriage'.

Since it was mostly Josephine's money that had launched the project, she sought to impose her ideas on the running of the enterprise. Their differences deepened when the burgeoning tourist complex needed a concerted policy of development and firm management skills. Josephine was frequently absent, had little time for domestic issues such as schooling for the children or the hiring of staff, and had no patience with business matters. These tasks fell upon Jo.

A relatively trivial incident brought things to a head. Josephine appeared on a peak-hour television programme with some children to talk about Milandes. Jo was not present but watched the broadcast. For him it was the last straw.

'My name was not mentioned once,' he complained bitterly, 'yet I lovingly gave my name to the children Josephine brought back from all over the world.' Bouillon told journalists, 'I can't go on. I offered to divorce Josephine but she refused. She is afraid of a scandal.'

Their separation was, however, officially made public.

Later Jo explained, 'I didn't agree with the way Josephine managed the chateau. She often had to leave us for her work, but someone had to stay and look after the family and make the estate profitable. From her point of view, I should have quit my orchestra. I often told the children, "If Mother takes care of the home, I will go out to work."'

The ninth child to join the adopted family was a Guajiro Indian boy, just two months old, whom Josephine found in Maracaibo, Venezuela, in 1959. Josephine received the child on 22 April from the hands of his parents, Ricardo Fernandez and his wife Juana, both of the Epiayu tribe. They had serious financial problems and could not support the boy. The child was immediate baptised in a Roman Catholic church and given the name Mara, after a famous Indian chief of Venezuelan legend.

Josephine later admitted that she had a great deal of trouble in persuading the Venezuelan authorities to let her take the boy. They didn't want her to take an Indian away from his country before he could speak his own tribal language. She argued that he was too young to speak any language but that as an Indian he was the only true representative of the country. She had set her mind on adding an Indian to her collection and she achieved her goal. One can only imagine her exercising her considerable powers of persuasion, and charm, to get her way with local officials.

(In 1973 Josephine returned to Maracaibo with the then fourteen-year-old Mara, proudly proclaiming that he now spoke three languages, French, Spanish and English. She said that there was no school in the world where Mara could have learned Guajiro. Josephine had frequently affirmed that it was her intention to return her children to their native land to acquire the language and culture of their forebears.)

Josephine's frequent departures for Paris or abroad on tour, and her sudden reappearances, gave life at the chateau a spurious excitement. The children grew up in an atmosphere of both privilege and privation. Josephine was more possessive than a natural mother, but she could also appear to be angry and severe. She overindulged them with presents from faraway places, but scolded them for reported misdemeanours. During her absence they found affection where they could and became used to strangers staring at them and photographing them at play. If there were serious domestic problems they were hidden from public view. As their numbers grew they became the most photographed family in France.

It was with an air of triumph that Josephine paraded each new acquisition before visitors. Photographs of the period show healthy, well-dressed groups of youngsters with their parents at play in the grounds of the chateau, at supper in the kitchen, or at bedtime in their dormitory.

Josephine had always promised to have the children taught about their respective countries of origin, in the language of their parents. But elementary schooling in French was first necessary and legally obligatory. When they attended local primary school they were mocked by their fellow pupils, because, unlike the other children from nearby villages, they came from 'the big house on the hill run by the strange dark-skinned lady'.

In fact, Marianne, the sixth child to be adopted, who later married and had two daughters of her own, remembers receiving blows from other children at the Castelnaud-Ceyrac communal school, when she attempted to defend her brothers and sisters. They were all known as 'the adopted ones'.

As word spread of the transformation taking place in the tiny Périgord hamlet of Milandes, journalists from Paris began to make the journey to the south-west to see for themselves. They found Milandes to be more than two kilometres from the nearest local railway station on a little-used secondary line. No regular buses linked the centre to the nearest towns. A taxi taken in either direction meant paying double fare. For tourists and casual visitors the 'World Village' seemed cut off and remote.

On arrival at the village they found the centre divided into two distinct parts; on high ground overlooking the river valley, the chateau, together with two hotels, a 'museum', and some houses variously named *Ma Tonkinoise* or *J'ai Deux Amours*. Below the chateau, beside the river was a park with swimming pool, small golf course and dance hall. At the gates to the park (entrance 150 francs) postcards and souvenirs were on sale including ashtrays inscribed *Jo et Jo*.

Visitors noticed that Milandes lacked the usual amenities associated with a typical small French village. There was no local store selling general supplies or a café-bar. Those seeking refreshment were left with the choice of the two hotels, both owned by Josephine. A 500-franc menu was on offer[*].

The village square, named after Josephine, was adorned with a standing statue of her surrounded by a group of children clearly of different racial origins. The saintly pose of the statue offended some people because of its 'Biblical posture'.

The 'Jorama' wax museum was devoted to the cult of Josephine Baker. For 10 francs, visitors could follow her career in

---

[*] In 1960 the new French franc was worth f100 old francs, due to de-valuation.

life-sized tableaux, beginning with Josephine as a child in adult clothes dancing in their basement at home. A caption read,

> At the age of six in St. Louis, Missouri, she heard a voice which told her: 'Go and spread the message of understanding and love.'

The whole ensemble of chateau, park and attractions resembled what today would be called a 'theme park', conceived and run by a single management. The theme was twofold: a multiracial family of adopted children run by the artiste, Josephine Baker.

Chapter Eight
A Farewell – Olympia 1959

Farewell appearances by prominent artistes are a familiar ritual. Often they simply mean 'Au revoir', until the next time. The public crowd in to see their favourite personality, fearful that it may really be their last opportunity, and revel in remembering what he or she was once like in the springtime of their career. The artiste is reluctant to give up what Maurice Chevalier described as his 'tonic', that stimulus derived from contact with the audience, the applause, the adulation, and the reassurance that they are not forgotten. The connivance between performer and public creates the 'comeback', recalling memorable moments spent together…

Josephine's 'farewells' began in 1956, when from the stage of the Olympia music hall in Paris she announced that she was going to devote herself 'full-time' to her family. As that family grew, and the financial burden of the Milandes centre increased, a new emergency arose. With ten infants to care for and nearly one hundred dependent employees on the estate, Josephine realised that she had to go back to work. She telephoned Bruno Coquatrix, director of the Olympia, to bemoan her desperation. 'Something must be done. I can't wait any longer!' she cried.

Coquatrix, who had bailed out many an impecunious artiste, understood immediately. Within weeks he announced a Grand Revue called *Paris Mes Amours*, retracing Josephine's career and also the history of the Olympia from its inauguration in 1893. In two acts and forty scenes, *Paris Mes Amours* recalled Josephine's long route from St. Louis, Missouri, and the history of music hall in Paris. The opening night *répétition générale*, customarily attended by a specially invited audience of notables, was dedicated to the International League Against Racism and Anti-Semitism. The omens were good for Josephine's record 'comeback'.

The veteran theatre columnist, Thomas Quinn Curtis, wrote,

> The important news is that the beloved Josephine is again on the boards, with no melancholy talk of retirement this time – and that she has probably never had as great a hit in her spectacular career. She has never been better and she looks like a million dollars.

Making no concession to her fifty-three years, Josephine danced the Charleston and presented six new songs including a Harlem lament, *Pauvre Noir*, and a calypso number, 'Don't Touch My Tomatoes', as well as fronting ten ballet sequences. A headdress she wore, weighing six kilos and reputedly costing 60,000 francs, was an exact replica of the one she carried at the Folies Bergère thirty years earlier. Dressed as a gypsy fortune-teller, she descended among the audience singing *Donnez-moi la Main* ('Give Me Your Hand'), to offer well-rehearsed advice, to pat bald heads and stroke the fox furs worn by front-row spectators. It was an act she had perfected over the years and the effect was electric.

For eight months some 1,800 spectators applauded Josephine each evening at the Boulevard des Capucines. Many who saw *Paris Mes Amours* said it was the finest moment of her career. For some it evoked an earlier post-war epoch and they remembered Josephine's first leap to fame in Paris in the *Revue Nègre*. Others revelled in the reappearance of a form of Grand Revue they feared was in eclipse.

During the nightly interval in *Paris Mes Amours* Josephine received prominent visitors in her dressing room. Noel Coward, Marlene Dietrich, the Duke of Windsor, among scores of anonymous admirers, were ushered in to pay homage to the 'goddess of music hall'. President Charles de Gaulle sent her a bouquet of roses. Josephine's dresser lamented that the tears of emotional gratitude often ruined Josephine's make-up for the second act.

The critics, too, marvelled at the tenacity and courage of the woman who had so often been reported as being 'at death's door', who had acquitted herself as a patriot in the French Resistance, and who even then was attempting the impossible – to raise a multiracial family in the heart of the country, in a chateau threatened with closure for debt.

The Olympia season helped to alleviate the financial situation at Milandes. To a radio journalist sent to interview her at the theatre Josephine exclaimed, 'We've won! We're saved! Now I can face the future with confidence. I'm no longer afraid for my little ones.' The smiling faces of the 'Rainbow Tribe' looked out at her from photographs on the wall of her dressing room.

The Milandes tourist centre did indeed reopen the following summer, and Jo and Josephine made renewed efforts to save both their marriage and the business. But the reality of the financial situation could not be ignored.

The film director, Marishka, suggested making a film about the 'Rainbow Tribe' at Les Milandes, which at this time numbered ten, as another orphan, Jean-Claude, had joined the family. But when the moment came to sign a contract, Josephine refused, saying that she did not want her children to take part in a 'commercial enterprise'.

In January 1960 Josephine announced she was returning to the United States to perform. Despite having declared in South America that she never wanted to set foot in the country again, she said it was the needs of her eleven adopted children that made it necessary. The recent addition of the eleventh child, a boy named Noël, abandoned in Paris on 1 December, persuaded her to embark on another tour.

'Josephine is not angry!' wrote the American columnist, Art Buchwald in Paris. When he asked her if she did really say she never wanted to go back to the United States, she replied, 'I was misquoted... I did say America wasn't a free country because of the way they treated Negroes, but I think things have improved a lot since then.' She added, 'I think all my troubles started with my fight with Walter Winchell...'

By high summer in 1960 a crisis was developing, with mounting debts and estimated monthly losses of several million francs. (The house orchestra kept in attendance cost 5,000 francs a week but brought in barely 200 francs a day.) With Jo Bouillon mostly absent in Paris and taking no further part in running the estate, Josephine tried to manage everything herself, without listening to the advice of local farmers.

'You'd think we wanted to replace her on the stage of the Olympia,' one of them complained. 'Of the twenty-seven head of cows, eleven were due to be retired, but without Josephine's written authorisation they cannot be inseminated, slaughtered or sold,' he explained, 'and when the sow gave birth to a litter of piglets she wrapped them in a fur coat to protect them from the cold!'

Josephine's troubles were now at home in France. Her adopted family, aged from two months to eight years, were an increasing worry and burden while she was trying alone to maintain the estate in the face of growing debts. She sorely missed the managerial presence of Jo, who was now living in Paris.

Josephine's mission to bring up adopted orphans with Jo remained their sole tie, since he was legally their adoptive father. Although he kept a room at the chateau he no longer took any part in the management of the estate. Josephine bitterly recalled her words when they had embarked upon the enterprise. 'With Jo I want to make Milandes something that will be spoken about in the four corners of the world. When I am no longer here, what I have built will remain in France, a country I dearly love, because France understood me, brought me up and gave me everything.'

Josephine Decorated

For a brief few hours in August 1961, the mounting financial problems of Milandes were put aside, when Josephine was decorated in a formal ceremony for her wartime services to France. Six high-ranking military officers, including Air Force General Martre, and a former government minister, arrived in helicopters from Paris for an open-air ceremony and garden party in the grounds of the chateau. The staff and employees were joined by villagers and their families from the surrounding district led by the Abbé Tournebise of Castelnaud.

Dressed in the smart uniform of a lieutenant of the French Air Force, Josephine received the Medal of the Resistance, the Cross of the Liberation and the insignia of a Chevalier of the Legion of Honour (awarded in 1957) from the hands of General Martial Valin, representing General de Gaulle, President of the Republic.

After a few words from Air Force Minister, Pierre Bloch, recalling Josephine's services in the Free French Resistance, and a formal exchange of salutes, the representatives of the United

States, Spain, Morocco and Norway, conveyed the compliments of their respective governments. Josephine's eleven adopted children dressed in their Sunday best suits, then presented her with bouquets of flowers and the day took on the character of a family gathering in the shadow of the mediaeval walls.

As the champagne flowed, Périgord farmers met Parisian personalities and bemedalled veterans exchanged their souvenirs of the war, while eleven children marvelled at the accolades accorded to their adoptive mother for the role she had played twenty years earlier – something they could barely comprehend. As the children looked on, bemused by the formality of the occasion, Josephine escorted her distinguished guests through the village crowded with neighbours and well-wishers. It was the epilogue to a chapter of her life no one could have foreseen and no one who was part of it would ever forget. Jo Bouillon, her husband, was absent in Paris that day.

L'Arlésienne

Following its inauguration as a holiday centre, Milandes had, thanks to Jo Bouillon, been the setting for a number of sporting and musical events. Canoe racing on the river and greyhound racing in the park were attractive to locals and tourists alike. Later, fashion parades from Paris and a Chinese Evening brought notables and their wives from nearby towns. A Festival of Jazz and Twist attempted to exploit the latest dance craze from the United States as French pop singers seized on the 'twist' motif. (France's Johnny Hallyday sold a million copies of his record *Viens danser le twist!*)

The chateau and its grounds offered an ideal ready-made setting for such summer events. Remembering her brief pre-war success in Offenbach's *La Créole*, Josephine presented an open-air production of Bizet's operetta *L'Arlésienne*, based on Alphonse Daudet's 'Provençal' melodrama of unrequited love.

While creditors were beginning to tighten their hold on the estate, funds did not allow a full orchestra to be hired. Tambourine players from Provence dressed in traditional costume joined pre-recorded music and a cast of eight actors from Paris, including Jean Davy and Jacques Charrier of the Comédie

Française, combined to present a kind of 'sound and light' show of the operetta.

The story tells of Frédéric, whose tragic love for the girl from Aries ends in suicide. The girl never appears, but her mother, Rose Mamal, has a big emotional scene in the last act when she mourns her lost son. It was a non-singing part ideally suited to Josephine's histrionic talents and she gave it all she knew. The performance was followed by a torchlight procession and dancing through the village streets.

The Milandes production of *L'Arlésienne* was so well received that Josephine persuaded Bruno Coquatrix to present it in a two-week benefit season at the Olympia in Paris. This was a mistake. Under a warm evening sky below the walls and turrets of the chateau, the music and story of *L'Arlésienne* had found its perfect setting. Transported to Paris and played against poor scenery, the magic was lost. It failed to draw many spectators and was taken off. It was Josephine's last appearance in such a theatrical role.

Washington March

In 1963 Josephine toured both South and North America. It was while she was appearing in Lima, Peru, that creditors at home in Milandes began agitating for payment of outstanding bills. They were advised to wait for the return of the 'chatelaine' before initiating any legal proceedings.

In August Josephine flew to the United States to take part in a civil rights march on Washington. Her visa for entry into the country was obtained through the intervention of Senator Edward Kennedy.

Conditions for black Americans had improved slightly – on paper. There were now more black people in the north of the country than the south, and their voting rights were protected by a Civil Rights Act passed by Congress in 1957.

On 23 August, some 250,000 Americans responded to a call by six prominent black spokesmen, including Martin Luther King, to take part in a march on Washington. They gathered to claim their citizen rights in voting, jobs, housing, integrated schools, and they demanded the full application of Civil Rights laws. The crowd moved from the Washington Monument to the Lincoln

Memorial and heard Martin Luther King give his celebrated address that included the words, 'I have a dream…' The *New York Times* reported the event as 'the greatest assembly for the redress of grievances that the capital has ever seen'.

Josephine was there in her military uniform and medals of the war years. Surveying the vast mixed crowd of white and black citizens she exclaimed, 'Salt and pepper – just what it should be!'.

But she also felt a foreigner in her own country. Some people said she had been absent in France when most of the struggle for equal rights had taken place at home. Her public espousal in 1952 of the Argentinian leader Juan Peron, and his wife, Eva, had not been forgotten. Her popularity with Negroes had also suffered from the apparent discrimination she demonstrated in taking two white husbands and enjoying a lifestyle of comfort and privilege while her black brothers and sisters were suffering.

A few weeks after the march on Washington, four black children were killed in a bombing incident in Birmingham, Alabama, the home of the US steel industry. Martin Luther King arrived hours after the incident to calm the crowds, but no strike at US Steel was declared… That same year militant blacks found it necessary to openly fight for the desegregation of schools in Little Rock, Arkansas.

In 1963 Josephine began a new fund-raising assault on the US with a series of concerts at the prestigious Carnegie Hall in New York. All proceeds of *An Evening with Josephine Baker* were devoted to four different Civil Rights organisations and to her own project, the College of International Brotherhood.

At a press conference at the Hilton Hotel before the opening night, Josephine proclaimed herself to be 'a citizen of the world' rather than an expatriate American. She described Milandes as a 'camp for children of all races who live together' and suggested, 'if children can, maybe grown-ups can too…' It was mild talk for the outspoken champion of racial togetherness, but she had promised her agents to maintain good humour and not say anything that would be seen as a provocation.

The Carnegie Hall season was a triumph of balanced programming. Weaving musical links in two languages, Josephine paid homage to America's Helen Morgan by singing 'Bill', the song that artiste had made her own. The French standard, *La Vie en Rose*, was presented in memory of Edith Piaf who had died in France a few days before. There followed *La Seine*, 'April in Paris', *J'attendrai*, and of course, *J'ai Deux Amours*. The *New York Times* critic wrote, 'Every phrase she sang, every word she spoke, was delivered with an unfailing sense of theatrical values.'

Creditors Gather

As the financial situation of Milandes became acute, in June 1964 the creditors foreclosed on the estate and announced that unless Miss Baker could raise the two million francs needed to pay off the debts, the furnishings of the hotels and restaurants would be sold at public auction, to be followed by the buildings of the tourist complex.

As creditors closed in for the kill, Josephine launched a public appeal for funds. At a candlelit conference in the chateau to dramatise her plight she confessed that, failing help, it was the end for her 'Rainbow Tribe' of eleven orphans and the international colony. She revealed it would take two million francs to stave off creditors and appealed to well-wishers to open special 'Save Les Milandes' accounts in banks in every country so that her 'world village' symbolising fraternity could continue.

In answer to questions Josephine claimed that she and Jo Bouillon had invested their savings of three million francs to develop the tourist centre to provide income for the children until they were grown up. She said she didn't earn enough money herself on occasional singing tours to support a large family. In tears, she said gas, electricity and water had been cut off from the village because of unpaid bills. The children and villagers were going down to the river to draw water...

As news of the crisis spread, the media began to play its accustomed role. France's most popular actress, Brigitte Bardot, made a television appeal for funds to save Milandes and the children. The blonde film star, already known for her concern for animal welfare, told evening television audiences, 'Miss Baker's problem is overwhelming. Everyone should give Josephine as much help as they can, so she can keep her home and children with her. Josephine was always generous. Do the most you can for her...' An unprecedented number of people responded to Bardot's appeal, among them prominent personalities.

The foreign press seized on the story of the 'falling star' who had so often hit the headlines as singer and wartime entertainer. Large and small amounts of money by cheque and bankers' order began arriving at Milandes. King Hassan II, the Japanese Foreign Minister, and Cuban President, Fidel Castro, were among early contributors. The Hungarian-born American cinema actress, Zsa-Zsa Gabor, made her donation from Hollywood, while a 'substantial cheque' arrived from a group of Dutch donors. Pledges of help were also received from England, Germany, Switzerland, the Netherlands, Sweden and Denmark.

Within hours of Brigitte Bardot's appearance on television, viewers had telephoned enquiries and some 20,000 francs in money orders was received. Within a month of the Bardot appeal Josephine was able to announce that there was 'a good chance of saving the village'. She said an international committee was being set up to run the commercial side, adding that it was composed of 'people who know about business...' When Josephine's solicitor deposited a cheque for an undisclosed amount in the local court, delay was obtained and no auctioneer's hammer fell on 9 July.

The temporary reprieve allowed Josephine to set off once again on journeys abroad that might result in more substantial financial support for her community. She flew to Morocco to meet King Hassan II in Fez, and on her return to Paris announced, 'The King has saved our home!' She said the Moroccan monarch had promised an annual donation for an indefinite period to take care of the children. 'I am on the right road now.'

Stellina, a Moroccan born in France, became the second girl and youngest member of the Tribe, taking the number up to twelve.

Josephine had always had a weakness for people in high places. Just as she had been impressed by Benito Mussolini and Juan Peron and his wife, not to mention Marshal Tito and Madame Golda Meir, so she now fell for the Cuban revolutionary leader, Fidel Castro. She had been invited to attend the Tri-Continental Conference in Havana in January 1966, which grouped together more than two thousand delegates from Asia, Africa and South America.

It seemed a good occasion to promote interest in her project for a College of Universal Brotherhood. On arrival she made an appropriate declaration, saying, 'The conference is symbolic of what I always have wished for humanity, the understanding of all continents without any kind of prejudice.'

She promptly sang for sugar-cane workers in the fields and delegates alike, and was received by Castro, who gave her a bear-like embrace and invited all the children to stay for a July holiday on the occasion of the 7th anniversary of the Cuban revolution.

Josephine's visit to Cuba was cut short by sudden illness, a recrudescence of her former wartime intestinal trouble. She flew back to Paris with Jo from Buenos Aires in their first reconciliation in two years. She was ordered a pre-operation rest in Milandes and entered a private Paris hospital in February. The three-hour operation called for a period of convalescence at the chateau. Jo paid the hospital bill and flew back to Buenos Aires where he had emigrated to open a French-style restaurant. He promised to send some money to help pay debts incurred. During her hospitalisation in Paris, Castro sent Josephine a bouquet of roses and orchids.

There was one disconcerting note during this dramatic episode: the journalist, Jean-Claude Mazeran, affirmed that during her hospitalisation in Paris the cards accompanying flowers from well-wishers bore not one single well-known name in the music hall or song profession. '*Pas un seul grand nom du spectacle!*' he insisted.

But if the entertainment profession appeared to have forgotten her and was too preoccupied with its own affairs, the public continued to show its affection for Josephine with numerous letters and visits by those who remembered her in earlier days. Her life was out of danger but the chateau was still threatened with bankruptcy and closure.

When it was all over Josephine returned to Milandes and her chronic financial problems.

A few months later she received a reprieve from the bailiffs. The chateau, which was to be auctioned to pay off Josephine's debts, was temporarily saved when her solicitor deposited an undisclosed sum in the local court. The source of the money was not revealed. Some may have come from her recent tours. And Jo Bouillon may also have contributed.

Crisis – The End of a Dream

The year 1968 was the turning point in the long agony of Milandes and of Josephine's fortunes. Despite the annual influx of tourists to the region, it was nothing near the 140,000 visitors that Milandes had received in 1950. With Jo now living in Buenos Aires and the children scattered in boarding schools or homes, only a skeleton staff remained at the chateau to maintain the estate and installations. As the financial situation steadily worsened Josephine made a desperate last-minute attempt to stave off disaster.

The idea of a film about Milandes was suggested. But who would raise the money and write the scenario? And could Josephine adapt her enthusiasm for her unfulfilled project to the constraints of a commercial film? A new album of songs was brought out featuring a new lyric dedicated to Milandes. Entitled *Dans mon village* ('In my Village'), it tells the story of a group of youngsters growing up together in a storybook village.

Josephine was financially ruined and legally bankrupt. Instead of selling off parcels of land and buildings to defray running costs, she held on to the entire estate and, in consequence, was faced with compulsory sale of the ensemble in various lots. As during other times of personal crisis, Josephine's obstinacy asserted itself. She pretended not to hear the voices of reason and preferred to wait for a miracle.

Sale and Eviction

The sale of Milandes and the eviction of its owner was a tragi-comedy worthy of the French boulevard theatre. On the one side, an ageing star with a family of orphans trying desperately to hang on to a chateau in the face of mounting debts; on the other side, property developers and speculators waiting to seize the estate. When the law was brought to bear on creditor's claims, legal niceties prolonged the fight and gained the defendant numerous reprieves. When the final verdict was announced, village gendarmes, burly workmen and a public prosecutor joined in an unseemly brawl reminiscent of tales of Provence by Pagnol.

Creditors' claims against Josephine had begun as long ago as 1963, when two local contractors, father and son, decided to press for payment for building work carried out in 1957. Josephine was touring in North and South America at the time and the authorities withheld action until her return. The welfare of the infants in her care helped to weigh in her favour when appeals for funds were launched.

Under French law Josephine was clearly bankrupt and the sale of her main asset, the chateau, was her main resource. But the law allows reasonable delay and forbids expulsion during the winter months. Instead of moving out after a final Christmas gathering, Josephine persisted in hanging on in a gesture of defiance.

Josephine's last fight for the survival of her family in Milandes began in earnest in February 1968, when a forced sale by public auction was announced at Bergerac district court. Twenty lots comprising a chateau, hotels, an amusement park, as well as a farm and outbuildings, were on offer. At the five-hour auction the chateau was 'sold' for a quarter of a million francs, a ridiculously low figure for an estate valued at around eleven million. When a better offer was received by the court the sale was annulled and Josephine was allowed two months to find a backer before a new auction. Her debts were estimated at 2.5 million francs.

As he had done in the past, Bruno Coquatrix came to the rescue. He hastily announced Josephine's appearance at the Olympia. She would top a variety bill beginning in April. It was Josephine's first return to the capital in four years, a fact that would please both old and new fans. Receipts would go to help stave off the seizure of her home in the Dordogne.

To packed springtime audiences, Josephine sang such traditional numbers as *Avec* and *Demain*; she literally belted out 'I Could Have Danced All Night' and 'Hello Dolly!', and nearly caused a riot when she sang and danced a Charleston to 'Yes, Sir, That's My Baby!'. Coquatrix planned to bring her back again when booking permitted. He also saw that Josephine would be ideal in a French edition of *Hello Dolly*!

Josephine's two-week engagement would have continued into

May but for real riots taking place in the Latin Quarter of Paris. French students were holding the government to ransom for reforms and the Sorbonne University was occupied by a sit-in. The country was in a turmoil. As President de Gaulle hurried back from an official visit to Romania, Coquatrix decided to close the theatre rather than risk involvement in the disturbances. Josephine promptly left on a tour of Scandinavia.

On 3 May, the Milandes chateau and estate were again put on the auction block. In two hours it was all over; the whole estate was knocked down for 125 million francs. Josephine, who was performing in Göteborg, Sweden, was informed by telephone. The Stockholm evening paper *Aftonbladet* announced 'Dream Destroyed As She Dances' and the *Expressen* quoted Josephine as saying, 'I am an idealist. And ideals and business don't mix.' She bitterly recalled that the domain had been valued at 663 million francs only three months before. The chateau alone was worth 200 million and it had gone for a mere 28 million.

Bruno Coquatrix was not among the final bidders, as Josephine had hoped. Her eldest adopted son, Akio, attended the auction and was shocked at the way their home had been disposed of among businessmen, at the stroke of a hammer.

Josephine had been given until October 1968 to vacate the chateau which had been sold at the auction. She arranged to move to a small apartment in Paris with the children, but she had not given up hope of reversing the court order to leave the premises. Believing she had been cheated, she hired a Paris lawyer to find a way of abrogating the sale, perhaps on a legal technicality.

On her return to France Josephine's domestic troubles were overshadowed by the political fallout from the French student riots and events in the United States. In April the black American activist, Martin Luther King, had been assassinated in Memphis, Tennessee, and in June the American Senator, Robert Kennedy, was shot dead in Los Angeles. Both events moved Josephine and she remembered how Kennedy had helped her to obtain a visa to visit the United States in 1963.

After taking part in a march down the Avenue des Champs-Élysées in support of General de Gaulle (she had donned her military uniform and medals for the occasion), Josephine gathered up five of the children and flew off to the United States to attend Kennedy's funeral. In view of the continuing efforts to save her chateau and provide for the children's future housing and education, it seemed to many people to be an unnecessary extravagance.

On the Friday following the sale Josephine left Milandes for Paris while the three new owners of the chateau, the restaurant and the hotel, took possession of their respective purchases. The main purchaser moved in to the first floor of the building.

To everyone's dismay Josephine suddenly reappeared in the village during the weekend and calmly walked into the grounds of the estate. Despite joint protests from the new owners Josephine entered the ground floor of the chateau and installed herself in the kitchen.

Josephine then summoned two gendarmes from the nearby village of Domme. On their arrival Josephine made a formal complaint that the court order for her expulsion did not take effect until 15 March, and that the new owners were in violation of the law. The gendarmes duly noted her complaint and left.

The following day workmen employed by the new owners forced their way into the kitchen where Josephine had slept the night and physically ejected her while she was still wearing her nightclothes. In the ensuing commotion the public prosecutor from nearby Bergerac arrived and confirmed that Josephine had indeed until 15 March to quit the chateau, and that if she chose to spend the remaining days in the kitchen she was legally entitled to do so.

Josephine was by now suffering from nervous exhaustion. Her obstinacy in refusing to accept her inevitable departure from her beloved chateau was against all reason and her symbolic return was an act of hopeless desperation. The resulting image of Josephine sitting on the back steps of the kitchen in her nightclothes, surrounded by a few personal belongings and food and drink, was the final symbol of a woman fighting a lost cause.

The Monaco Rescue Operation

Owing to Josephine's celebrity the plight of her family of orphans had been observed throughout the world. Wherever she had performed people read of her efforts to save her home and create the multiracial community based in the mediaeval French chateau that was her home. For most observers it was a story of misfortune and mismanagement and they were incapable of coming to her aid. In France most people knew better than to interfere where the law was involved. Those closer to the scene of struggle knew of the recklessness with which Josephine had embarked on her adventure. They were only sorry for the innocent children who were about to suffer from the eviction. One person who lived relatively near to Milandes was well placed to come to Josephine's aid.

Princess Grace of Monaco, the wife of Prince Rainier of the Principality of Monaco, was not only a former American film star with an understanding of an artiste's temperament, but she was also President of the Monégasque Red Cross, which held a prestigious annual fund-raising gala in Monte Carlo. Grace had been present at the Stork Club in New York when Josephine had been humiliated in public, and she had followed the rise and fall of Josephine's fortunes. Here was an opportunity to help a fellow American artiste and at the same time indirectly bring humanitarian aid to the children through the Red Cross.

Josephine was invited to top the bill at a 1969 gala organised by the Société des Bains de Mer and produced by a young and talented theatrical designer, Andre Levasseur. The versatile French actor, Jean-Claude Brialy, would be Josephine's presenter and compère. The event would offer Josephine a unique showcase to display her talents before a select international audience.

It was a risky gamble to choose a star sixty-three years old to entertain sophisticated audiences more used to seeing young top-liners in their prime. As a cynic remarked, for an artist over sixty, every extra year counts double! But both Levasseur and Brialy were confident that Josephine had all the qualities required.

In Paris Josephine turned her attention to a new short season at the Olympia entitled *Paris Mes Amours*. Her small two-room accommodation was within easy reach of the theatre and her neighbour was Marie Spiers, the wife of Pierre Spiers, her musical director. Marie Spiers ran a small dress shop in a fashionable quarter of the city. When Pierre Spiers noticed how badly dressed Josephine appeared offstage he asked his wife to dress her and not count the cost. The big fashion houses that had once been glad of Josephine's custom had begun to refuse her credit.

Visitors to Marie Spiers' shop were sometimes surprised to see a pair of legs sticking out on the floor below the curtained changing booth. They belonged to Josephine who was having a short nap after the exertions of the previous evening's performance. A few days after the last night of *Paris Mes Amours*, Josephine had a stroke and was hospitalised. It was the first of three that would cause concern for the rest of her life. Marie Spiers would remain Josephine's close friend and confidante to the end.

In May 1971 Josephine was received by Pope Paul in a semi-private audience in the Vatican. The Roman Catholic Pontiff praised her efforts on behalf of abandoned children. The Vatican announced that the Pontiff expressed admiration for her talent as an entertainer.

Josephine and the Cinema

People have often asked why Josephine did not make more films. Her career in the cinema was brief and sporadic. In the half-dozen films in which she appeared, only three were sound features, and only two, *ZouZou* and *Princesse Tam-Tam*, offered any scope for her talent as an actress. Her last appearance on the screen was in *Fausse Alerte*, completed in 1940. It made little impact when it was released in 1945, or in the US in 1950, entitled *The French Way*.

Josephine never made a film in Hollywood. Her professionalism was never in question in whatever she undertook. Roles for dark-skinned performers were few. The American film industry was slow to accept black characters as part of contemporary life and they were still confined to stereotyped roles.

A former fellow artiste, who knew all about Hollywood and Josephine's long road to stardom, then came to Josephine's aid. As the former film actress, Grace Kelly, Princess Grace of Monaco was also the President of the Principality's Red Cross. She promptly offered to accommodate the dispossessed family in a private home in Monte Carlo.

During the following months Josephine and the children settled down to a new way of life in Roquebrune, a hilltop commune overlooking the bay of Monte Carlo. Under the protective authority of Princess Grace, Josephine and the family of adolescents began to adopt a natural way of life that had escaped them in Milandes.

Dressed modestly in everyday clothes, Josephine went down to the market every day with her shopping bag and became an anonymous resident of the community. She took the children to the cinema occasionally and tried to put behind her the long misadventure of Milandes. But secretly she never gave up hoping that her dream of her Brotherhood College would one day come into being.

Chapter Nine
Golden Anniversary

To celebrate her golden anniversary in show business, from when she had made her debut on Broadway, Josephine returned to the land of her birth in June 1973 to give five shows at the prestigious Carnegie Hall in New York. It was fifty years since she had first drawn attention to herself in *Shuffle Along*, and nine years since she had last performed in the States.

Josephine strode onto the stage of Carnegie Hall in spangled tights under a monumental headdress of pink ostrich plumes and, striking a provocative 'Ooh-la-la' pose, asked, 'How do you like my Eiffel Tower?' The audience gave her a two-minute standing ovation. Mocking her sixty-seven years, singing 'Look at the ole' girl now, fellas…' (from *Hello Dolly!*), she brought the house down.

Josephine's one-time agent, Stephen Papich, recounts, 'It was the old Josephine. It was the feathers and the sequins and the gold dust and the diamond dust. It was furs and egrets and towering headdresses and jewellery. She wore dungarees and rode motorcycles and cracked jokes and conducted the orchestra. The audience went crazy for her. It was something!'

Nor did she neglect to 'rap' with the audience and say it all again. 'People must live together as human beings, not as "black people" and "white people" and those other unimportant things…'

Audiences forgave her earlier outbursts of anger against the system. Those who sympathised with her fight against discrimination admired her for her courage. The columnists had had their fun playing with her fiery spirit; some had been burned in the process. Here was a veteran who had earned their respect.

The same show went to Los Angeles, San Francisco and Detroit. In Los Angeles, Josephine made a triumphant appearance at the Ahmanson Theatre of the Music Centre. Frank Sinatra and Bob Hope were appearing at a benefit performance a few steps away at the Pavilion Theatre. While their show was only half attended, two thousand people were turned away from seeing Josephine. She had made it at last, and returned to France happy despite her earlier hurts. It was not her last visit to the US but her big show at Carnegie Hall had brought her the acclaim she had dreamed about.

Despite her triumph in America as an ageing superstar, Josephine was still not immune from critical comment or even indifference in unexpected quarters. The following year she returned for two brief dates in New York and Los Angeles. A slovenly production at the Beverly Hilton, Beverley Hills drew the following sharp comment in *Variety*:

> Baker's act isn't worth waiting for... A watered down version of a show in its full glory at the Ahmanson several months ago... the performance was chaotic and disorganised, an assemblage of random rambling, missed cues and muffed lyrics... Baker, even when at her best, is strictly a nostalgia trip for those who remember her Parisian heyday and are willing to apply considerable imagination to current attempts at song and patter... Every now and then, the old Baker voice will come through in a rousing song finish; occasionally there is glimpse of appealing good humor. But her unsteadiness and self-exaggeration of her own style still overwhelms.

Was it perhaps that age was at last taking its toll, and that those rousing moments would be the exception rather than the norm? Teamwork and production have always been an essential part of Josephine's appearances, as the following incident shows.

Josephine was booked to appear at the Palace Theatre in New York in a show opening on New Year's Eve 1973. Management indifference pervaded the engagement. An outdated poster advertising the theatre in Times Square still showed Bette Midler, not Josephine Baker, as did the bills in the theatre itself. A dutiful reporter from *Esquire* magazine, Dotson Rader, arrived from early morning to follow the dress rehearsal through to the opening. His story reflected the atmosphere of the event and of Josephine's tiredness.

Under the headline, 'Down, But Not Out At The Palace', Rader recounts in column after column how 'Josephine Baker copes with bored musicians, recalcitrant stagehands, and the toll of years'. His interview is permeated with wistful sadness, as though Josephine's heart is no longer in her appointment with her New York audience.

From behind enormous protective dark glasses she gives uncoordinated replies to questions, mixed with fragments from the past and remarks about lazy musicians and a dirty stage.

'The band have only two songs ready. Only two songs...! You could not even wash the floor for Josephine? You could not even do that?' she bitterly remarked. And Rader notes,

> The strain was partly due to the fact that the attitude of everyone seemed to be one of patronizing or ignoring the star. One felt that from the stagehands to management representatives, they believed they were doing Baker a favor by hanging around. Moreover, that she did not deserve the favor.

Addressing Rader in a motherly manner, Josephine says at one point, 'I must tell you, son. I'm a woman whose life was lived by what I said, you see? All of a sudden the bottom fell out my life. I was thrown out of Les Milandes by eight young men paid ten thousand old French francs each. You must write that down. There in the mud Josephine was thrown. It was raining. That's where you belong, they say. They throw my animals at me. I love animals and I cry. I was alone. I was old...'

And so on, in unrelated phrases, she relived her eviction as though it was happening again, there and then.

The journalist was stunned and the report ended by reading like an obituary, but it showed the dignity of the artiste confronted by stagehands unwilling even to throw a switch for her. Full of compassion for the woman he had been sent to report on, Dotson Rader writes,

> And I thought, she wants to stop now. She wants to throw it over. It is too late, and she has done the act too often. She is an old woman now, and worn through by the years, and she is among

people who pay her no regard, do not understand what she remembers of life, who think she is over the hill. Time for your travellin' shoes, sweet Josephine.

That night the show went on as usual. It was not a full house. A third of the audience was black, which is what she liked. Once again Josephine received a standing ovation. But the champagne she ordered for after the show failed to arrive. So she sat alone in her dressing room, on New Year's Eve!

South African Tour

Towards the end of 1974, Josephine was invited to tour in the Republic of South Africa. It was her first and only visit to the country whose overwhelmingly preponderant black, coloured and mixed-race populations were ruled by a small minority of white settlers. Josephine could scarcely have been unaware of the situation of racial separation prevailing, but the terms of her engagement were attractive and she needed the money. There was no mention in her contract of performing before segregated audiences, because that was the accepted way of life under the apartheid laws. Her visit was not without incident.

In Cape Town, minutes before her appearance at the huge Three Arts Theatre, a bomb threat was received. While the building was hastily searched her compère vanished and the management wore faces like sheets. Josephine refused to leave the building.

'Do they forget I was so many years in the [French] Resistance?' she asked. 'They can't frighten me with threats!'

When nothing was found Josephine sailed out on to the stage with her usual poise and sang. Critics swore that she appeared to be not a day older than twenty-two!

In Durban a group of black friends was refused admission to see her perform, despite appeals to the authorities. Josephine reportedly became 'sick' over the incident, saying, 'They could have sat in the balcony which was empty.' A doctor was called to calm her distress. 'If I had known things were as bad as they are, I would never have come to South Africa,' she complained.

At the completion of the tour, houses had been a quarter full at all performances and the impresario had lost money from the engagement. Josephine left for Paris saying she would 'speak out on what she had seen and experienced'. Compared with the attitude she had adopted in the United States, it was a mild rebuke. 'Surely the time has come for people to say "We have had enough" and reach out their hands to their brothers?' she pleaded. 'Otherwise it will be too late.'

The journey to the continent of her ancestors was the last she would make beyond Europe.

As the years passed Josephine became more outspoken on racial issues. She put aside formerly limpid declarations of 'universal brotherhood' and began to use her celebrity status to make pronouncements openly on personalities and politics. She freely expressed her admiration for the Cuban leader, Fidel Castro, and her dislike of Richard Nixon before he became US President. Whereas before she had willingly lent her name to anti-racist and anti-Semitic organisations, she now expressed reserve over Black Power and professed to detect a new intolerance in the movement. She acknowledged that black people are often racist, even among their own communities. 'All power is power,' she declared. 'I don't like discrimination. I'm shocked when I hear our own saying "black people this, black people that". It just shows we haven't come very far.'

Royal Variety Performance

In November 1974 Josephine was the sole female star at the Royal Variety Performance at the London Palladium. Graced by Royal presence, the gala evening was preceded by a week of special matinées. It was Josephine's first appearance in Britain for seven years. She was supported by a bill of international performers, including The Hungarian State Dance Company and the Harlem Dance Company, the first black ballet company to achieve a truly international status.

Josephine was in good company and readily concurred with the Harlem Dance director, Arthur Mitchell, who said he had started encountering prejudice at auditions early in life. 'The best way to combat that is to be better than everyone else,' he told journalists.

The columnist in the London *Stage* wrote,

> She still retains that extraordinary quality which can take a huge
> edifice like the Palladium, reduce it to the intimate scale of a Paris
> bistro and make 3,000 people a fistful of putty in her hand.

Josephine was in her element in London and never better singing
songs in French and English on the huge Palladium stage. After
the performance she was presented to Queen Elizabeth, the
Queen Mother.

The Last Call

Back in Paris preparations went ahead for the Paris opening of
Joséphine, the retrospective of her life and career from St. Louis to
Monaco. The one-hour version of her career in song presented in
Monte Carlo had been well received, and backers had been found
to present a more elaborate version in Paris. The 'rags to riches'
story of the black girl who taught the world to Charleston had all
the ingredients to please sophisticated Paris audiences, who were
critical of mediocrity but respectful of sustained talent.

It was to be a three-hour revue illustrating Josephine's career
in sketches and songs, played by comedians Laurence Badie and
Annie Sinigalia, with Jean-Marie Proslier as compère. Josephine
as a teenager in the *Revue Nègre* would be played by Richild
Springer. The book of the revue was written by the Montmartre
poet, Bernard Dimey.

Many well-wishers would have liked to see *Joséphine* at the
Champs-Élysées Theatre, where she had made her debut on the
Paris scene fifty years before, or even at the Folies Bergère or the
Casino de Paris. Long-term commitments by the managements
there prevented this, and huge resources and insurance would
have been required, far beyond the three-million-franc budget
available. The medium-sized Bobino Music Hall in Montparnasse
offered a more intimate framework for the revue and carried less
commercial risk for the promoters.

The Bobino was a very Parisian 'neighbourhood' theatre
seating 1,100 people, in the narrow Rue de la Gaité, traditionally a
street of popular entertainment and pleasure dating from the
previous century. It seemed an ideal venue for such a nostalgic
return to the roots of the music hall. To honour the occasion the
auditorium of the Bobino was completely refurbished for

Joséphine.

This hundred-year-old *cafconc* or café-concert hall was rooted in one of the older quarters of Paris and had always been frequented by amateurs of French song. Originally it was where one drank and talked while hard-working performers tried to keep the attention of the audience with songs and repartee. It had resisted conversion into a cinema and had remained a music hall, not so large as to distance spectators from the artistes, yet big enough to accommodate more than a thousand people. Nearly every notable French music hall artiste had performed there: Chevalier, Trenet, Piaf, Montand, Reggiani, Barbara... It would be Josephine's first appearance on its stage and her name dominated the facade of the theatre.

Josephine at the Bobino

On Monday 24 March, *Joséphine* was given a try-out at the Bobino Theatre before specially invited guests of the Paris evening newspaper *France-Soir*. It was easy to fill the theatre with guests, but the question was, would the paying public come to a small left-bank music hall to see an ageing star recall her past successes? Theatre director Jean-Claude Dauzonne and his team kept their fingers crossed and waited for the reaction. They had the full support of the theatre owner, Jean-Pierre Bodson.

Within days of word going round that a unique event was taking place in Montparnasse, seats were sold out for weeks ahead. As the management's confidence grew, minor adjustments were made to the songs and sketches and critics and journalists were invited to see the revue before the official opening. Their reports were ecstatic. They praised both Josephine and the Bobino for their courage and initiative in putting on such a sumptuous revue.

The gala opening of *Joséphine* took place on Tuesday 8 April, in an atmosphere of intense excitement. Fashionable *le tout Paris*, including many prominent personalities in French public life, converged on the small neighbourhood music hall, so different from the large right-bank auditoriums. A congratulatory telegram from President Giscard d'Estaing was read out from the stage. It acknowledged Josephine's 'universal talent' and spoke of a 'grateful France whose heart has so often beaten with yours...'

Older members of the audience were particularly moved to see an artiste nearing seventy carry off the evening's entertainment with such style and elegance.

Josephine made her entrance in a white lace-stitched robe and immediately received a prolonged standing ovation. She was to make numerous rapid costume changes throughout the evening, notably into a tight-fitting white trouser suit which admirably showed off her slim figure.

Joséphine was not a one-woman show, but a show written around one woman whose career spanned half a century of music hall. The fifteen scenes, comprising ten sketches and thirty-four songs, followed in quick succession, tracing the long road she had travelled from childhood in St. Louis, with a glimpse of her American heritage, through her leap to stardom in Paris and on four continents, until war brought life to a standstill and she joined the French Resistance. A military jeep on stage recalled that Lieutenant Baker entertained Allied military forces in North Africa, Europe and the Middle East, until she set up a home for orphans in south-west France.

American vaudeville tradition was respected with the appearance of a black child (Celia de Souza Rezende, an eight-year-old from Rio de Janeiro) to whom Josephine sang, not 'Sonny Boy', but 'Sonny Girl'! Writing in the *International Herald Tribune*, Frank Van Brakle wrote,

> Josephine sings with equal ease in French and English, plus one song in Portuguese and 'My Yiddisher Momma'. The voice is as warm and strong as ever, although, understandably, not as sure as it once was in the upper ranges. But the stage presence is there, along with complete professionalism that marks her every move and the sure-fire ability to communicate with the audience.

In the office, Dauzonne and Levasseur relaxed, believing they had a hit destined for a successful run. Their mood was strangely reminiscent of the relief felt by Daven and de Maré when Josephine had headed the *Revue Nègre* in Paris fifty years before. Events had come a full circle and the omens were good.

As *Joséphine* settled down to an assured season in Paris, plans were being made to take the revue to London and New York.

Meetings were scheduled with lawyers and agents, and Josephine's optimism knew no bounds. Few of her immediate circle dared to express doubts that an artiste who was nearly sixty-nine could sustain a new arduous tour abroad.

Meanwhile, French and foreign visitors to the Bobino were delighted to rediscover the star of their youth, trim and poised, apparently unchanged as though the years between had not existed. Josephine had kept the weight, figure and shapely legs she had possessed when she was nineteen.

For younger members of the audience it was a revelation and a lesson in music hall history from a veteran. Josephine's story of half a century of song and dance had all the ingredients of a popular nostalgia trip. A flurry of renewed interest in music hall was confirmed when another, slightly younger performer, Charles Trenet, announced his own retrospective of songs to be presented at the right-bank Olympia Music Hall.

At the close of each evening's performance, with its South American song selection and then the *Paris–Paname* finale, repeated as a encore, Josephine and the company received a standing ovation. Many of the audience, with fond memories of Josephine's earlier triumphs, wanted to congratulate her personally, but limited space backstage had ruled out admitting visitors to the dressing rooms. Instead they were invited to wait in the lighted auditorium. As the evenings lengthened, crowds also waited outside in the street to see Josephine cross the road to dine on mussels or spaghetti with other members of the cast. Josephine's return to the Paris stage had coincided with Easter and the city was in a holiday mood.

The End

The end, when it came, was swift and not entirely unexpected. Following a reception for three hundred people at a Paris hotel, Josephine was believed to be sleeping late the following afternoon. When the telephone failed to respond for an interview with a journalist, it was discovered she had suffered a heart attack. The morning newspapers she had been reading hours before were left strewn about and still in a coma she was rushed to the Pitié-Salpêtrière hospital.

Alerted by telephone, her sister, Margarette, and Princess Grace of Monaco were present at her bedside, together with Marie Spiers and two black nurses. Her doctor indicated that there was little hope of recovery. Members of the Bobino team stood around in shocked silence. All knew that the show, and Josephine's long performance had come to an end.

As old files of photographs were reopened, the Paris Sunday tabloid, *France Dimanche* (which had once anticipated Maurice Chevalier's death by one week on its front page), gave Josephine its accustomed treatment reserved for royalty and pop stars. JOSEPHINE AT THE END OF HER STRENGTH, shouted the black headline over a six-column picture of the artiste lying in the ambulance that took her to hospital.

Josephine died late on Saturday afternoon, 12 April 1975. The doctors confirmed the cause of death as cerebral haemorrhage caused by a severe heart attack. Margarette bathed her sister's body and dressed it in the white muslin robe she had worn at the gala. Photographs were forbidden and the coffin was closed and placed in the hospital's chapel.

Josephine's death was reported throughout the world. From the staid (and slightly inaccurate) *Times* obituary in London to the pages of lurid colour photographs in the South American press, editors scoured their files to recall a life that seemed to belong to another age. Critics and commentators recalled her stage career and anti-racist stance and her self-appointed humanitarian mission for racial equality.

André Frossard in the French *Le Figaro* wrote,

> She dreamed of gathering around her unhappy children from the entire world and offering them a chateau, normal in the land of make-believe but not in Europe. For the rest she counted on her lucky star which still shines, and on others, which comes to saying, on whom she couldn't depend.

What did Josephine mean to her adopted children? Frossard then asked.

> A big sister, a slightly whimsical charitable dame of unexpected kindnesses, maternal concern or a nest of feathers? They will be

surprised to learn that this strange woman was famous for her legs and not for her arms.

As the legend and anecdotes resurfaced, Josephine's image again became that of a Thirties music hall artiste, adorned in feathers and sequins, arms outstretched, frozen centre stage in an attitude of universal embrace, until the curtain fell and the lights were switched off. Beyond that narrow definition given by the media very little of the real woman emerged in the obituaries.

In an unprecedented gesture to a foreign-born artiste, Josephine was given a State Funeral at the huge church of St Mary Magdalene in the centre of Paris. (Commonly known as 'La Madeleine', the Greco-Roman style temple was built to honour Napoleon's armies, and was once nearly turned into a railway station before becoming a fashionable church. Its ornate pediment carries sculptures depicting the Last Judgement but the church is still today without the customary cross on its summit.)

On the damp grey morning of the funeral, 25,000 people gathered in the Rue Royale in front of the church to pay their last respects to Josephine. As the funeral cortege moved from the Latin Quarter to the right bank, it stopped briefly in front of the Bobino Theatre where Josephine's name came alive in lights for the last time, exactly one week after her memorable triumph there.

In the church, adorned with lines of French flags and one of the Stars and Stripes, some two thousand people packed the aisles to await the arrival of her bier. Representatives of the government, the army and the Resistance had joined prominent members of the entertainment profession and countless anonymous mourners. Josephine's estranged husband, Jo Bouillon, had arrived from Buenos Aires to join three of their adopted children and other family members. The flag-draped mahogany coffin carried floral tributes from the French President, the Bobino Theatre, and a huge cross of roses and lilacs inscribed *Papa and the Children*. Also on the coffin were her military decorations resting on a blue cushion, and a floral Star of David.

The officiating priest reminded the congregation that 'Christ died twenty centuries ago as poor as a slave, and Josephine was the daughter of slaves...' Canon Thoren continued, 'What an extraordinary adventure her life was, from the poverty of her beginnings in Missouri to the glamorous and prestigious career that spanned half a century.' Appropriately, music was part of the Mass, with Mozart's *Requiem* setting the tone. There was a hushed moment when the strains of 'Sonny Boy' floated over the congregation played by Pierre Spiers on the harp, to be followed by the melody of *J'ai Deux Amours*, forever associated with Josephine's life and career.

Josephine died as she would have wished, in Paris, presenting her life in music and song. As someone was said to have remarked, 'She died of joy.' Her funeral was remarkable for the muted emotion it evoked of how a little coloured girl from Missouri could capture the heart of a nation and be so honoured. Yet of the thousands who gathered at the Madeleine, no white-haired former admirer broke ranks to throw a rose on the coffin... no militant anti-racist publicly offered to continue her struggle... no young theatrical aspirant stepped in the path of the cortège... Paris absorbed the event, as it has many others, with equanimity and unruffled dignity. This was not the case at Josephine's subsequent burial in Monte Carlo.

Despite her often proclaimed affection for France, Josephine had expressed the wish to be buried in Monaco, her most recently adopted home. It may have revealed a certain bitterness and disappointment over her loss of Milandes. At all events, Roquebrune was her home and the burial service was to take place in the church of Saint-Charles in Monte Carlo. She was then to be buried in the local cemetery. But even in death Josephine was to find no rest.

The night following the funeral, Josephine's mortal remains were taken to Monaco for burial in the Principality where she had so recently taken up residence. The masses of floral tributes did not accompany the coffin but were distributed throughout Paris at monuments to the victims of two world wars and to Jewish deportees. Josephine's body was admitted to the Athanée Chapel in Monte Carlo to await a simple burial service. In accordance with Josephine's wishes only her immediate family were present on the Saturday: Jo Bouillon, her estranged husband, Margarette

Wallace, her sister, and the twelve adopted children, with Princess Grace in attendance.

At that point things came to a standstill. As news of her final resting place was circulated, many people who had not attended the funeral in Paris wanted to pay their last respects at her grave. They were to be disappointed. Weeks after arrival in Monaco, Josephine's coffin lay unattended in a chapel of repose, locked and inaccessible to outsiders.

In the coming months the cemetery of Saint Charles was visited by hundreds of people who had come from afar to lay flowers on her grave. They too were destined to be disappointed. When enquiries were made of the Monégasque Thanatologie Company responsible for the cemetery, the reply was, 'We are waiting for orders from the mayor's office or the Palace.'

Once again, even in death, Josephine's misadventures were grist to the press. The cemetery of Saint Charles has but 2,500 burial spaces. In such a money-conscious town the fee to unlock the door to such a privileged resting place overlooking the sea is high. Josephine had to wait her turn. The press pertinently demanded to know where those who proclaimed their loyalty to the artiste were…

The woman whom the world had clamoured to see in life now appeared in death as an encumbrance to those who had courted her. After nearly six months' wait her burial finally took place in October. The black granite tomb and headstone, donated by Princess Grace, bears the following words:

Josephine Baker – 1906–1975

Epilogue

Throughout her career, Josephine Baker was an easy subject for journalists, critics and biographers. Most dealt, in varying degrees, with the three main aspects of her life: her brilliant theatrical career, with its ups and downs; her unexpected wartime service in the French Resistance; and her abortive attempt to establish a multiracial community in France. Her strong anti-racist sentiments ran through her entire public and private life.

From the very beginning of her career in America, Josephine was recognised as 'good copy' by the press. At first they were captivated by her irresistible clowning; much later, journalists were to feed on her misfortunes. Her contrasting moods, ranging from euphoria to depression and anger, were the raw material of the media. But the numberless comments, articles and interviews rarely examined the motivating source that drove her, often beyond reason, to live such a turbulent life. Josephine herself admitted, 'I always repeat the same things at interviews... It's practical, since journalists write what they like.'

Josephine courted the media and never shied from publicity of any kind. From the moment she first appeared on the stage she was eager to be noticed and talked about; later she unashamedly shared her penury and grief in public. The widely published image of Josephine sitting shoeless in the rain, on the kitchen steps of her sequestered chateau, said more for the woman than the justice of her eviction.

Her celebrity as an artiste offered her the chance to live comfortably, but her tireless energy led her to pursue her self-imposed mission – the adoption of orphans of different nationalities. Even though the Milandes project failed, her struggle to come to terms with her own identity and her fight against racial discrimination continued to the end.

During the Second World War, Josephine could have avoided all involvement in the conflict and returned to America. She chose instead to put her health and safety at risk to aid her adopted country that had welcomed her at the start of her international career.

As an exotic dancer, she had enflamed people's passions, but her turbulent lifestyle discouraged a settled domestic existence. Her failed marriages were no more exceptional than those in other professions. She died during the fiftieth anniversary of her Paris debut, a civil rights activist still carrying the flame of her chosen vocation.

After her death, interest focused on those who were able to throw light on her earlier years. Family members and professional associates became the target for writers seeking to understand more fully the woman behind the facade of the veteran music hall artiste. The few books that followed attempted to identify the source of her energy and draw together the traits that made up her character.

First in the field of biographers was her last husband, Jo Bouillon, who collaborated with journalist Jacqueline Cartier to present a life entitled simply *Josephine*. Bouillon, who had been with Josephine for little more than ten years, and Cartier, had inherited forty files of handwritten notes in French for her (eventual) autobiography. Even with the help of a professional writer, Josephine herself would have found it difficult, if not impossible, to tell her story with any degree of objectivity. Latterly, she resembled that most prolific of writers, Georges Simenon – one of her former lovers – at the end of his career. Josephine could no longer separate fact from fiction and freely lent her name to the fabrication of fable and legend.

At the time of her death in 1975, a number of people who had known Josephine well in her early years were still living in France and abroad. Their reflections were a valued addition to the legend that had accompanied her career.

Caroline Dudley, the widow of the French writer, Joseph Delteil, recalled the adventure of bringing the young unknown dancer to Europe. As an enlightened American, she saw in Josephine someone who could further the experience of Negro music and dance.

Their brief association was not without consequences for both of them. After losing her protégée to an astute French impresario, followed by a legal battle with Paul Robeson to replace her, Dudley forgave Josephine for having accepted a rival offer of engagement and devoted herself to her husband's literary life. As she watched Josephine's rise from afar, she admitted a grudging admiration for her courage and determination, but she never returned to the hazardous task of promoting black artistes.

When Josephine crossed the Atlantic for the first time, at Dudley's invitation, she crossed the 'Waters of Lethe' to put the past behind her. The Washington-born musician and composer, Duke Ellington, had also experienced the restorative effect of travelling to Europe.

'You have to be a Negro to understand why,' he said. 'You can go anywhere, do anything, talk to anybody... You can't believe it!' (For all that, it did not stop someone telling the Duke that if he had been a white man he would have been a great musician!)

As Josephine often remarked, 'From the moment I arrived in Paris it was like a dream. Paris made me what I am. I owe everything to her.'

The veteran designer, Paul Colin, who shared Josephine's celebrity after receiving her in his Paris studio, readily acknowledged his debt to the young dancer who had inspired him. He revealed to her the beauty of her own body and his poster of her helped to make her famous. He understood the role of the media in promoting her career, and the stridency of Afro-American dance infused much of his later work. The few films in which Josephine appeared failed to exploit her potential as an actress and merely concentrated on her exotic image.

Marcel Sauvage, Josephine's first biographer, living in retirement in Nice, remembered his audacity in trying to write the life of a nineteen-year-old American *métisse*. As a newspaperman, he caught the innocence of Josephine's spontaneous observations, and his poet's ear captured the jumbled thoughts that tumbled from her lips. His youthful instinct was rewarded when his book went into several revised editions (with Paul Colin's designs) but he left it to other writers to enlarge on her later career. He did, however, devote an entire new chapter to Josephine's experiences when making her three feature films, in an enlarged new edition of his biography published in 1949.

Margarette Wallace, Josephine's sister, living with her adopted daughter in a 'grace and favour' flat in Monte Carlo, recalled that there had been a secret pact between her and Josephine since their childhood in St. Louis, to come to each other's aid if the need arose. Uprooted from their native Missouri to help Josephine's growing adoptive family, Margarette viewed with mistrust those who sought her out as one of the last surviving members of the McDonald-Martin family.

'All the books that have been written about Josephine are full of lies,' she declared vehemently. 'She loved Jo [Joseph] and Jo loved her. It was a love match. Josephine loved the children, all of them. She spoilt them. She was too good to them. One day I am going to tell the truth…'

Josephine had the unique ability to move people and to elicit sympathetic understanding at first contact. As one of her former agents, Felix Marouani, remarked, 'Josephine either adopted you at once, or not at all!' She was artless and impulsive in her relationships, direct and pitiless in her dislikes. She was incapable of deception and inspired confidence in those she liked. Her innocence was a virtue, until the livelihood of others was involved. She could fight for her own interests, because she knew she could deliver what was expected of her professionally. But when the less scrupulous elements took advantage of her, she could not reconcile sentiment with pragmatism. Therein, perhaps, lies the cause of the collapse of Milandes.

Josephine's reaction to people she met was direct and spontaneous. She immediately assumed they were on her side until it was proven otherwise. Her effect on others was equally instant and often long lasting. Her apparent openness deterred people from looking below the surface. Everything about her seemed immediately accessible. The list of those who fell under her spell is long. Josephine's musical director and composer, Pierre Spiers, affirmed that no one could remain indifferent to her, and he paid tribute to her implacable professionalism.

France's famous poet and songwriter, Charles Trenet, admitted that he had once written a youthful verse to her when he was fifteen. Ada Smith Ducongé, alias 'Bricktop', remembers that

Josephine simply brought out the mothering instinct in her; while Jean Clément, Josephine's one-time hair-stylist, broke down in tears when he showed the writer early photos of Josephine. The American columnist, Janet Flanner, who wrote under the pen name of 'Genet' in the *New Yorker* magazine, admitted that she rewrote her original account of the *Revue Nègre*, for a later compilation, because she had earlier underestimated the importance of that theatrical event in 1925.

The most senior of those who had known and worked with Josephine, Mathilde Légitimus, whom Josephine had befriended in the *Revue Nègre*, was the matriarch of a family of actors and dancers working from Paris. As a French West Indian, 'Baby Darling' – as she was then known – understood better than many the hurdles and obstacles Josephine had surmounted during her trip down the long road of her career. She was also the most frank and perceptive about Josephine's character.

It had been said that Josephine was inclined to be racist among others of colour; that she jealously defended her position, as a black artiste among whites, as a kind of revenge against her own race. As a woman who had struggled for herself and her family, Madame Légitimus felt impelled to tell the truth about those tumultuous days when black and coloured artistes fought to achieve professional dignity. In the simplest of terms, Mathilde Légitimus told the writer, 'Josephine didn't like her own race very much.'

Josephine's racial origins and childhood experiences in St. Louis conditioned her life. Her preoccupation with 'racial equality' runs through her entire career, emerging at inopportune moments, complicating her personal relationships, and causing the cancellation of lucrative theatrical engagements. Her innate talent and determination carried her to the top of her profession, but even after she had become rich and famous, she remained oversensitive and vulnerable to racial slights.

As Western attitudes evolved, she identified herself increasingly with those of mixed racial origins. In struggling to reconcile the different traits in her character, Josephine revealed herself to be a woman of dogged determination, open-handed generosity, and almost suicidal obstinacy. She fought to the end for what she believed and suffered greatly in the process. Blessed with an iron constitution, a series of illnesses only made her more determined to continue her struggle against racial discrimination of every kind wherever she believed it existed. Her stage career became both a means to an end (to support her adopted family) and an end in itself.

As Josephine became famous and rich, she also became 'white' in many people's perception of her. Which is to say, people forgot or conveniently put aside their prejudices when the object of their discrimination achieved star status. But with endless world tours, punctuated by seasons in Paris and abroad, the years were slipping by. She was not, as Mistinguett was, dedicated to the theatre to the exclusion of all else. Her warmth and gregariousness led her to seek more permanent relationships outside the scope of the theatre; a husband, and rediscovering her vocation as a wife and mother.

All four of Josephine's marriages failed and her numerous amorous adventures left little discernible trace. However, an early love affair with a young Frenchman named Marcel may have sparked a personal revolt.

Even in Paris, the world's most exotic city, he refused to marry her 'because she was black and a dancer'. He cited his parents, his job, and 'what the world would think' as reasons for refusal. 'You can't change the world,' he told her.

Josephine's reply was, 'The world must change so that class enmities and racial barriers end. I *will* change the world!'

Josephine then knew instinctively that she must attain a certain status in order to be able to fight for the change she called for. There arose in her the coloured person's determination to succeed by whatever means. In a white world that meant gaining money and status. The pattern that then emerges is of a troubled, torn spirit, striving to attain excellence in her profession.

First, she had a ready-made legend of a black girl who escaped an oppressive environment to cater for the demands of the entertainment industry. After surmounting discrimination within the profession, she was confronted by greater selectivity within the ranks of professionals internationally. There, too, she acquitted herself with credit.

Josephine left no theatrical legacy behind her. The traditional role of *meneuse* in French music hall, which Mistinguett had perfected, was doomed from the 1950s. (Line Renaud and Lise Malidor gallantly tried to prolong the role in revues at the Casino de Paris and the Folies Bergère, but parody had already replaced the authentic presence of a 'vedette'.) As Michel Gyamarthy told the writer, sitting in his office at the Folies in 1982, 'There are no vedettes any more!'

Josephine's appearance at the Bobino Theatre in 1975, backed by a lifetime of experience, was the final flourish of a popular art form. So electrifying was her presence that the veteran actor, Michel Simon, celebrating his eightieth birthday, was moved to climb up on to the stage to embrace Josephine on her opening night. In the standing ovation that followed, the golden age of French music hall could not have received a more appropriate accolade.

For all the aura of artistic endeavour surrounding Josephine and her circle, none of her twelve adopted children entered the entertainment profession. Few of them even saw their mother perform on the stage. Perhaps the children were suspicious of the stress and anxiety behind the facade of ritual family reunions after each arduous tour. However, while giving convincing appearances of domesticity in Milandes, Josephine was unconsciously acting a role against a theatrical mediaeval backdrop. The children's age and generation placed them beyond reach of the epoch Josephine represented in the theatre. Instead, they became passive players in an intrusive media circus that developed around Josephine and the chateau.

Only Jean-Claude Baker, who was never himself a member of the 'Rainbow Tribe', later made a name for himself in American radio and television. But he was neither a natural son nor an adopted member of the family. In a reversal of roles, he had adopted Josephine and her name, and served as her secretary and companion during her last concert tours.

A young French Corsican, inexplicably moved by the news of Josephine's sudden death, devoted years of travel and research into meeting Josephine's surviving family and associates. *La véritable Joséphine Baker* by Emmanuel Bonini reflects the emotions of many who knew her. His book is a valuable contribution to understanding the woman.

Noble Sissle, the orchestra leader and former vaudeville performer who helped Josephine at the beginning of her career, paid tribute to his protégée's humanity.

> Josephine Baker never allowed her spirit to grow up. She has kept her heart young, always filled with a deep spiritual force, forever grateful to people for what they have done for her and deriving great pleasure from doing things for others without expecting publicity or personal gain.
>
> Her tenderness of heart and true humanitarian spirit places her in a rare category. She is deeply aroused over racial bigotry and human injustice everywhere and had devoted much of her time to fighting racial discrimination. Her triumphs debunk the old adage that 'a prophet is without honour save in his own country'. Josephine Baker is truly an international apostle of goodwill and human equality.

A perceptive critic of the French music hall, Louis Léon-Martin returned to the source of Josephine's European career when he wrote, 'One cannot separate Josephine Baker from the *Revue Nègre*.' And in a single paragraph, he sums up her durability.

> Josephine Baker never renewed her act. She gave us all she had from her first appearance. With unfettered ecstasy and instinct, she is incapable of guiding and watching over herself... She is a force of nature... She is also the expression of a civilisation, a new contribution, an unknown delirium, and that is why one cannot write about contemporary music hall without according her due place and paying tribute to her.

When all is said and done, an enigma remains: where did the springs of her energy and determination come from? She mastered almost every situation she confronted until, at the summit of her career, physical exhaustion took its toll. Despite her celebrity, she never wavered in her belief and never abandoned her mission: to unite people of all races, colours and creeds. Her weaknesses were those of someone struggling to change the world single-handed. Others with greater means have achieved much less, while Josephine gave of herself entirely. Her generous devotion to the human condition remains an example to all.

Selected Bibliography

Abtey, Jacques, *La Guerre Secrète de Joséphine Baker*, Paris, Éditions Sibonet, 1948

Aulnet, Henri, *Le Music-Hall Moderne et les Revues à Grand Spectacle*, Les Presses Modernes, 1936

Bizet, René, *L'Époque du Music-Hall*, Capitol, 1929

Bogle, Donald, *Toms, Coons, Mulattoes, Mamies and Bucks*, USA, Bantam, 1974

Bonini, Emmanuel, *La Véritable Joséphine Baker*, Pygmalion, 2000

Bouillon, Joseph, *Josephine*, Laffont, 1976

Bresler, Fenton, *The Mystery of Georges Simenon*, New York, 1983

Derval, Paul, *Folies Bergère*, Les Éditions de Paris, 1954

Flanner, Janet, *Paris was Yesterday*, New York, 1972

Georges-Michel, Michel, *Nuits d'Actrices*, Les Éditions de France, 1933

Hammond, Bryan and O'Connor, Patrick, *Josephine Baker*, Cape, 1988

Harding, James, *The Ox on the Roof*, London, Macdonald, 1972

Jacques-Charles, *Le Music-Hall*, Édition, 1950

Léon-Martin, Louis, *Le Music-Hall et ses Figures*, Les Éditions de

France, 1928

Prasteau, Jean, *Casino de Paris*, Denoël, 1975

Rémy, *Mémoires d'une Agent Secret*, Paris, Éditions aux Trois Couleurs, 1945

Rivollet, André, *Une Vie de Toutes les Couleurs*, Grenoble, Éditions B. Arthaud, 1935

Sauvage, Marcel, *Les Mémoires de Joséphine Baker*, Paris, KRA, 1927
——, Marcel, *Voyages et Aventures de Joséphine Baker*, Éditions Marcel Seheur, 1931

Tabet, Georges, *Vivre Deux Fois*, Laffont, 1980

Verne, Maurice, *Les Amuseurs de Paris*, Les Éditions de France, 1932

Index